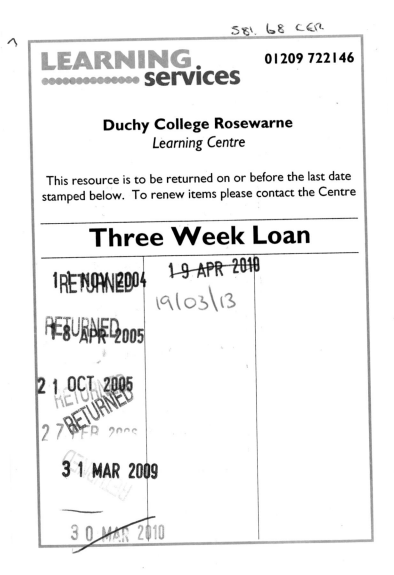

ENDANGERED PLANTS

Dwarf Forget-me-not
(*Eritrichium nanum*)

ENDANGERED PLANTS

By Jan Čeřovský

SUNBURST BOOKS

Designed and produced by Aventinum
English language edition first published 1995 by
Sunburst Books, Deacon House,
65 Old Church Street, London SW3 5BS

© Aventinum, Prague 1995

Text by Jan Čeřovský
Introduction and Postscript by Věroslav Samek
Translated by Elizabeth Kindlová
Photographs by Jan Čeřovský (41), Zdenko Feyfar (3),
Jiří Havel (7), Josef Hlásek (2), Petr Moucha (2),
Dušan Pangrác (2), Bohumír Prokůpek (4), Jan Ševčík (1),
Dušan Slivka (136), Jan Štursa (4), Zdeněk Thoma (1),
and Stanislav Vaněk (1)
Illustrations by František Severa
Maps by Jan Čeřovský
Graphic design by Antonín Chmel

ISBN 1 85778 101 5
Printed in Slovakia
3/20/05/51-01

CONTENTS

Shallow wetlands are among the most threatened biotopes in Europe and in the world as a whole. A wet
meadow in late summer when the most robust of the horsetails — the Great Horsetail (*Equisetum telmateia*)
— has appeared in full force.

INTRODUCTION

Extensive natural and semi-natural areas are still preserved in European mountains. The penetration of man the sportsman and holidaymaker represents a serious threat, so it is important to manage these 'leisure' activities by establishing national and nature parks.

According to the estimates of some biologists (precise data are not available at present) there are over five (perhaps as many as ten) million species of plants, fungi and animals in the world. It took millions of years of evolution to develop this enormous diversity of life on our planet. However, in recent years man has not been so careful in handling this wealth. Both directly and indirectly, his activities have impoverished this 'genetic bank'. In the last few decades alone, he has destroyed more organisms than in all the previous centuries. Many experts predict that by the end of this century about half a million to a million species will become extinct. This forecast is not just a warning. No-one can really estimate what sort of ecological and economic consequences might occur as a result of these losses, and no-one can imagine how nature and our entire environment will further evolve.

This ecological damage is affecting all organisms — plants, fungi and animals, some more than others. Of course green plants hold a special position in this respect, as the existence of all other forms of life depends on them. Only plants containing green pigment — chlorophyll — are capable of producing, with the input of light energy, complicated organic compounds from simple, inorganic matter (water and nutrients). These are essential for the nourishment of all animals including man. Mankind would not survive for very long under the present conditions if all plants were to be destroyed. In a very short time everyone would die of hunger. This is certainly the worst possible outcome and man, as the only animal gifted with sense — *Homo sapiens* — can prevent this. Of course today the excessive impoverishment of nature is leading to various ecological defects which mankind is repairing and treating in the most complicated way and at great cost. The vacant spaces, or niches, left behind by destroyed organisms are quickly being filled by opportunistic and assertive species, among which are many 'harmful' species from the utilitarian human point of view. As a consequence more and more widespread and destructive calamities occur in fields, orchards and forests. Man must suppress these, and this not only costs a lot of money but also requires a great deal of energy in the production of pesticides and their application. Moreover, many of these poisonous preparations can destroy other organisms, thereby causing a vicious circle.

Man made his entrance on the Earth's stage very late if one takes into account the entire geological time span — i.e. in a period when today's flora and fauna were already fully developed. At first he collected fruits and other parts of plants, hunted animals and caught fish or other water animals, and it was the ability to exploit the force of fire which distinguished him from the rest of the most highly evolved animals — primates. We know of man's existence in this role as far back as the middle stage of the last ice age, approximately 35—40 thousand years ago. At the time he was integrated into nature and did not stand out in any significant way. Several thousands of years later he had already 'invented' agriculture and began constructing the first settlements. It only took several hundred human generations to make the Earth too small for this species and for man to begin to conquer space. It was also around this time that this creature supposedly endowed with sense began, altogether senselessly and on a large scale, to destroy the natural wealth of his own planet. We have become used to calling our era the age of the scientific and technical revolution, but we can also call it an age of the genocide of other organisms.

The ways in which man influences nature are multifarious. Basically they can be divided into direct impacts and indirect ones. One of the direct and deliberate interventions is the gathering of plants. Particularly at the turn of the 20th century, 'herbalists' collected medicinal plants on a large scale, or to be more precise, plants which they claimed had curative properties. These were for example Arnica, Sundews, Spring Pheasant's eye, Gentians — the Spotted and Great Yellow Gentian. In recent years there has been a certain revival of 'natural medicine' and hence there is a fear that this activity may threaten some rare species. The plants most endangered by this activity are those picked for their root, bulb or rhizome; those species required for their stems and leaves are subject to a lesser threat.

A similarly dangerous phenomenon which is on the increase is the transplanting of ornamental plants from the wild to gardens. Thanks to the mobility of contemporary man, this 'gathering' activity is affecting extensive regions from lowlands to high mountain areas. Most damage is inflicted on those species which have an interesting colour and shape such as Saxifrages, Snowdrops, Gentians, Orchids, Waterlilies and many others.

Hiking and sport also contribute to the destruction of some plants. Hundreds of holiday-makers not only trample down rare species but also pick bouquets of flowers which they later throw away before they get home. This behaviour has an especially destructive impact on mountain flora because under harsh climatic conditions these species grow slowly and propagate with great difficulty. Likewise recreation causes destruction to many plants which grow on the sea coast, especially on sandy beaches.

The application of herbicides and fertilizers has a very unfavourable effect on rare species. Many plants cannot withstand this intervention and so Orchids, Gentians and other species are disappearing from meadows altogether. The same process, together with the replacement of traditional farming with modern technology which can separate the seeds of weeds from corn crops, has led to many formerly abundant weeds becoming a rarity on fields today and these must now be officially conserved. In central Europe these weeds include the Corncockle, Nigella and many others.

Many rare species are being destroyed by the construction of housing estates, factories and power plants, roads and new airports, open pit mines and quarries and other building activity. The mining of peat or bogs is also responsible for the disappearance of many rare species.

Already this brief overview indicates the widespread direct effect of man on nature. If anything the indirect effects are even worse for it usually becomes quite complicated to prevent the primary cause. For instance, the grazing of cattle is one of the indirect impacts. Of course, sensibly managed grazing, on the contrary, facilitates the existence of entire species because it provides them with the opportunity to take root in trampled soil or minimizes the competition of expansive species (e.g. some grasses). Even the excessive hunting of animals may directly or indirectly disturb the existence of many plants. Even pheasant's eyes, pasqueflowers and other species are disappearing from pheasantries, particularly in the spring, because the pheasants like to pluck the buds and blossoming flowers.

Among the 'hidden' indirect effects of man's activities is the application of pesticides. These may kill off specialized pollinators and many plants then lose the chance to reproduce successfully: the flowers are not pollinated and the seeds are empty. Pesticides as

well as excessive fertilization also often suppress the mycorrhiza of fungi with which many plants live in symbiosis. So-called mycotrophal plants cannot exist without fungi; so for instance more and more Orchids are disappearing from meadows.

The life of many rare plants is being greatly disturbed because of the drainage and reclamation of marshes and wet meadows. The drying up of the soil is leading to the disappearance of numerous rare species such as Squills and Orchids. The flora of marshes is also endangered by water flowing down into these land depressions from the surrounding intensively farmed plots, as this water contains excessive nutrients or even toxic matter (pesticides, etc.). So unintentional over-fertilization/eutrophication occurs in such marshes, as a result of which many plants cannot survive. Moreover, other plants which flourish on over-fertilization (e.g. ruderal species), attain high vitality and force out sensitive, usually rare species.

Eutrophication is also endangering many species of aquatic plants growing in stagnant or flowing waters. This mainly applies to waters in lowlands, in the agricultural countryside. In mountain areas another damaging factor is also appearing — water acidification. 'Acid rain' has now affected an extensive area of Europe (and the temperate zone) resulting in the death of forests, aquatic plants and animals from the Alps to Scandinavia. The waters of North America and other regions are also being affected in the same way.

Here we come to another factor which, especially in the last 2—3 decades, has been causing great damage to plants. This is emissions mainly resulting from the incineration of fossil fuels. 'Acid rain' is also affecting forests, particularly coniferous ones. The

death of forests is naturally accompanied by the disappearance of entire species of plants. In many areas even the omnipresent bilberry has been declining in number. In some areas the graceful Silver Fir, a symbol of Christmas, has completely disappeared and elsewhere its mass death 'fir decay' is continuing. 'Big' fungi are also suffering greatly because of 'acid rain'; in many mountain areas their wealth of species has declined by more than half.

We have mentioned only some of the main impacts of human activity which are leading to the impoverishment of flora and each one may have a far-reaching impact. However, this brief overview indicates the ways, and these are often very intricate and concealed, in which human activity is affecting nature. It is essential to recognize these effects and mechanisms and their impact so that we can effectively defend against them. However, it must be ac-

9

knowledged that science has not yet taken into consideration all the ecological and genetic ways in which nature has been and continues to be impoverished.

Various habitats and their plant communities are threatened in various ways. Plants in the greatest danger are those in habitats which are significant because they contain the greatest wealth of rare species. The various vegetation formations, listed according to the rate of danger, are as follows: xerotherm grassland communities — highland vegetation — peat-bogs — damp meadows — weed communities — coastal vegetation and maritime salt-marshes — woodland.

Each of these habitats and their plant communities is, of course, threatened by the results of specific human activities. Damp meadows are being affected by drainage or fertilization. Mountain vegetation is already endangered by hiking and mountaineering or even acid rain. The communities of peat-bogs and swamps are threatened by the extraction of peat, the weed communities by intensive farming technology and so on.

In order to formulate an effective strategy for the conservation of plants, it is important to know the level of danger and the processes which are causing the greatest losses in the regions in question. If the primary causes could be removed then the actual disappearance of organisms could be prevented.

There is one question on everyone's lips: What will happen when any of the species dies out? The answer of nature conservationists usually focuses on ethical and cultural arguments. Nevertheless the present process of 'phytogenocide' often has serious economic, ecological and even psycho-social consequences.

For example the death of Silver Fir (*Abies alba*) as well as some colonies of graceful Spruce (*Picea abies*), particularly those which provide resinous wood, means a substantial economic loss. The destruction of a certain plant species is really a 'biological desolation' resulting in the extinction of further organisms which directly or indirectly depend on the plant in question. The destruction of the fir signals the disappearance of, for example, *Polyporus (*tree fungus) which is dependent on this woody plant species and with it the beetles that live in this fungus. The decline in bilberries in forests is leading to the disappearance of Capercaillie because these birds not only live on bilberries but their young need the shrubs of bilberries for shelter. The destruction of plants initiates the increasing disappearance of dependent species. The impoverishment of countryside species leads to ecological destabilization and the disappearance of insect pests, pathogenic fungi etc.

Every species destroyed signifies a certain poten-

The beauty of mountain forests and meadows is created by irreplaceable mountain flowers: a colony of flowering Spotted Gentians (*Gentiana punctata*) on the margin of mountain spruce woods in the Protected Landscape Area of the Jeseníky Mountains in the Czech Republic.

tial loss which cannot be estimated financially. Today only very few plants from the entire wealth of species of flora are utilized by man (more in regions less economically developed than in industrially developed countries). If of the entire wealth of plants we are only familiar with the uses of a few, we cannot estimate how the hitherto unused species will be implemented in the pharmaceutical and cosmetics industries, in the production of pesticides and repellents in the future. One cannot exclude the possibility that among wild plants there are species which could even present a new source of nutrition. And what does the genetic utilization of plant species offer? As yet no-one has dared to state in specific terms the prospects of the utilization of genetic engineering. It can only be stated that the genetic loss represented by the extinction of a species or a population means an irreplaceable loss.

Therefore everything points to the fact that the species and genetic variety of the countryside is not a mere 'decoration' of our environment but is one of the supporting pillars if not the direct condition for the existence and further development of human society. Hence nature conservation is not a social luxury or the affair of voluntary amateurs. Effective nature conservation is imperative for a society to develop in a healthy way physically and mentally.

In most developed countries nature conservation is more or less effectively regulated officially. However it has been demonstrated that not even well organized official conservation can be effective without the help of volunteers and without the participation of the public at large. This is where the importance of conservational enlightenment comes in and where information such as that contained in this book can play a key role.

Official nature conservation usually includes plant and animal species protection and the designation of specific areas of conservation. Of course it is only possible to achieve this in practice with the discipline of the whole of society. The effectiveness of conservation therefore depends, to a significant degree, on public education, information and awareness. Everyone should be taught about the problems of nature conservation as well as about the actual danger to individual species.

The most effective plant conservation lies in area conservation — i.e. in the conservation of the entire community in which the species in question is found.

The protected areas are usually divided into small nature reserves, natural monuments, conservation areas or larger areas such as national and nature parks, protected landscapes and seascapes. On large protected territories there are smaller, more strictly protected territories, whereas on the other hand certain farming activity is permitted which should not significantly affect the natural character of the territory. However, some reserves must be managed by man to preserve the natural state which is the aim of conservation.

The second form of the conservation of organisms is species conservation. This occurs when certain plant species are officially protected against the destructive intervention of man. The conservation regulations vary (for example, the picking of flowers is allowed but not the extraction of entire plants). Sometimes this species conservation is accompanied by a 'ratebook' for the imposition of fines if conservation status is violated deliberately or through negligence.

Species conservation today is based on so-called red lists, which are lists of plant or animal species in various threat categories. More detailed data on the most endangered species are contained in red books processed on both a worldwide scale and for individual continents, states or even smaller regions (areas, districts, etc.).

The first botanical 'Red Data Book', published by the IUCN (International Union for the Conservation of Nature and Natural Resources), includes 250 endangered plant species from about a hundred countries. The data needs to be supplemented and redefined continually. This also applies to the European red list which was first published in 1977 and for the second time in 1982. According to this list, of the total number of about 11,000 vascular plants occurring in Europe, 10% of the species were endangered in the 1970s; at the beginning of the 1980s the figure went up to 30%. Although these two pieces of data are not precisely comparable because in the second edition the criterion of danger has altered to a certain degree, it does, however, indicate that the process of the endangerment of European flora is continuing.

Most of the red list in compliance with the world Red Data Book (IUCN) distinguishes the following categories of species: Ex — extinct species, E — endangered species, V — vulnerable species, R — rare species, I — indeterminate species, K — insufficiently known, O — out of danger species or species only known from old records. According to the decision of the 19th century General Assembly of IUCN, January 1994, the above categories should be revised and slightly changed.

Most regional red lists and red books keep roughly to these categories or introduce their own com-

Before man began to industrialize and pollute the countryside with chemical poisons, interesting and attractive European terrestrial Orchids (in the photograph: the Narrow-leaved Helleborine, *Cephalanthera longifolia*) lived in productive association with human management of the lands: today special care must be devoted to their conservation.

parable categories. Some even emphasize the categories of endemic species, i.e. species occurring only in certain, usually more limited phytogeographic regions. The endemic species are mainly rare and easily damaged because they are restricted in number. For example, of the total of its plant species the Alps region has about 8% endemic species, the Carpathians about 4.5%, etc. Some endemic species are often found only within several square kilometres (e.g. in the Alps) or even on several hectares of land (some species grow on serpentine ground,

etc.). In the most extreme cases only one surviving species is known to exist and if a power station or another source of damaging waste is built nearby, then it is probable that this endemic species will sooner or later be destroyed. Every nature lover is always pleased to hear that some 'red' data has changed to 'green' which means that the endangered species, thanks mainly to the care devoted to its conservation, has passed into category 'O' (i.e. out of danger). The red lists and books have spurred professional and amateur botanists to search for new, hitherto unknown localities of rare and seriously endangered species. It must be added that in many of these species, new occurrences have been identified, sometimes in altogether unexpected habitats such as railway cuttings or ditches. Elsewhere, on the contrary, an intensive search for rare and endangered species ends in the discovery that the species in question has become extinct at the last known locality. The only proof which remains of its existence are herbal items, photographs or slides.

Important as the red lists and books are for specific protection or even conservational measures, they are basically only the first step. Normally they only present the degree of danger but lack the analysis of negative effects and biological data which is essential for the protection and conservation of endangered plants. Hence today increasing attention is devoted to the biological research of rare and endangered species. Their site requirements (soil, climate) are studied as well as population genetics, propagation, extent, etc.

In 1973, under the initiative and management of the IUCN, the Convention of International Trade in Endangered Species of Wild Fauna and Flora, the so-called Washington Convention, was organized. By 1994, 122 countries had become members, 33 of these from Europe. The European countries, co-operating with the Council of Europe, organized the Berne Convention in 1979 which addressed the conservation of many animal and plant species. The importance of this agreement, in the annex to which 493 strictly protected plant species are listed, lies in the fact that the protection measures were extended to include not only certain species, but their entire natural habitat.

Each of us can contribute towards the conservation of endangered plant species. If, for example, a certain locality where a rare species is found is to be built up, drained or flooded by a new reservoir, then the endangered colony must be 'moved' to a new suitable site. A 'move' is achieved either by the sowing of seeds or transfer of the reproduction organs (bulbs, rhizomes, etc.) or of entire plants. This is demanding work and therefore it can only be carried out by conservation organizations normally under the direction of conservation institutions or various scientific institutes.

Elsewhere a population of rare species may be endangered by the constant decline in the number of individual plants. Such weakened population in the open countryside are strengthened by plants which are cultivated under unnatural conditions or by the alteration of soil conditions. Botanical gardens are usually involved in these specialized and complicated measures. The aim of our book is not to name all the conservation measures. We only want to show that the conservation of endangered plant species is usually very complicated to organize, financially demanding, requires profound specialized knowledge and usually also a great amount of manual work in which every nature-lover can help under special guidance.

Věroslav Samek

SEA COAST, MARITIME AND INLAND SALT-MARSHES

Chalk cliffs on the Baltic Sea (Jasmund National Park, Rügen, Germany): salt-loving plants colonize the narrow coastal strip.

At the turn of the 20th century when the first attempts at nature conservation were initiated, aimed at 'original, untouched' sections of the countryside, not many areas remained which were unaffected or even undisturbed by human activities. This included sea coasts. In the European network of protected areas today, some sections of the sea coast form a crucially important part. The United Kingdom, consisting of the island of Great Britain, Northern Ireland and many hundreds of islands off the British coast, has a very long coast line. Some parts of it, including some of the islands, are characterized by cliffs and steep rocky slopes. Protected chalk cliffs provide attractive scenery in several locations on the Baltic coast (e.g. in the Wolin National Park in Poland or in the Stubnitz Nature Reserve in Jasmund on Rügen island, Germany). The typical maritime flora and vegetation resistant to salty conditions is often found only in limited amounts on narrow coastal strips under cliffs.

The colourful mosaic of remarkable plant communities is however widespread on many extensive sections of flat sea coast. Sometimes only several metres difference in altitude can have a significant effect here on the representation of plant communities. It would take a difference of a dozen to hundreds of metres to achieve the same variation in inland areas. For example, a jewel of protected territory of this type is the European biogenetic reserve on the Dutch island of Terschelling; another is the entire region of Wattenmeer, stretching from the Netherlands through north-western Germany right up to Denmark, which is now a trilateral national park. These 'laboratories of life' hold considerable economic significance for the conservation and utilization of marine fauna (as well as for fishing) and for the conservation of migratory water birds. These areas also include Jersey in the Channel Islands; both Jersey and Guernsey are covered by the convention concerning World Cultural and Natural Heritage.

An important part of the ecosystems in these regions and territories as well as one of the important focuses of nature conservation are the varied and colourful plant communities. In Europe, particularly on the low-lying sea shores, nature is constantly changing the coastline, either by eating away the dry land, or elsewhere by building up the sandy and muddy deposits which are immediately inhabited by the first plant pioneers.

Many attractive plant species are to be found in maritime plant communities. Unfortunately many of them are already very rare and therefore belong to red list categories of the most endangered species and are officially protected. Their rarity and the continuing threat to their existence are due in part to natural factors but are mainly the result of human activities.

Until recently, long stretches of the European coast were not affected very much by human activities. However, recently recreational facilities on the Baltic and North Sea have been increasing. People build the sand into windbreaks on the beaches thereby disturbing the vegetation, destroying and stifling it. Large sections of the Baltic and North Sea coasts are also being developed with industries and housing estates. Apart from the space which they occupy, they are also a source of pollution. Furthermore the pollutants from the dry land are increased by pollution from oil tanker accidents and the dangerous storage of some waste in the sea.

This chapter focuses on several typical maritime salt plant species in need of conservation and these can be considered as representatives of several dozen

15

others. We are certain to come across some of them during a stay at the seaside. If you were visiting a nature reserve or other protected territory, you probably would not damage them, but the same care should also become a rule on recreational beaches or where the sea coast is our daily environment, our home or work place.

Likewise inland in Europe we come across plants which are dependent on the presence of salt in the soil — salt plants or halophytes — although normally, of course, in only limited areas. Some of these are species which occur in maritime salt marshes, as well as on smaller islands. We also find salt flora above all on alkaline steppes — the 'pusztas' of the Pannonian lowland in Hungary which also extends into the neighbouring countries of Slovakia and Austria.

In the past traditional farming of the land, particularly mowing and grazing, helped to preserve salt vegetation in inland salt-marshes. The present intensification or rather industrialization of agriculture, however, means that these habitats are disappearing rapidly. Most of those that do remain have only survived thanks to conservation areas.

A significant salt species found in maritime areas and inland salt marshes is the **Sea Plantain** (*Plantago maritima* L.) of the Plantain family. The leaves in a basal rosette are narrow lanceolate to linear, similar to the quite common Ribwort Plantain (*Plantago lanceolata*). However, when young the leaves are trough-shaped and, as is the case with many halophytes, rather fleshy. As opposed to the Ribwort Plantain, the Sea Plantain has a rounded, grooveless scape which bears a dense, cylindrical, green spike.

This 15 to 30 cm high perennial herb flowers in the summer (June to September) usually in salty meadows on the sea coast. Sometimes it also grows on marsh meadows inland where it is an indicator of saline soils. However, it is also known to grow in habitats with a chalky or travertine base.

The Sea Plantain is included in most central European botanical red lists under various categories of threat. Likewise some halophyte plant communities, to which the Sea Plantain belongs, are also considered as threatened. The reason for the decline is mainly the various 'improvements' to its habitat or the interruption of farming procedures which supported its growth or even made it possible in the first place.

On the island of Poel in the Wismar inlet in eastern Germany the marshy saline meadow with its rich occurrence of Sea Plantain and many other halophytes was declared a conservation area. However, once cattle grazing was stopped on this territory, important salt plants began to disappear. After a time the grazing of cattle in this reserve was renewed and positive results were attained over the next few years. Although the cattle consumes herbs requiring pro-

▽ The Sea Plantain (*Plantago maritima*) creates dense tufts of narrow leaves in basal rosettes: four stamens with bright yellow anthers protrude from dense spikes with brownish flowers.

The inland salt-marshes of central Europe (Pannonian ▷ lowland) have many halophilous species in common with the sea coast.

tection, especially the Sea Plantain, this does not seem to affect the plant; on the contrary, the number and vitality of its colony is increasing. Moreover a higher milk yield and quality of milk was discovered in the cattle grazing in this reserve.

In Britain, the Sea Plantain fortunately is quite common on all coasts.

The true beauty among plants of the European sea coasts is **Sea Holly** (*Eryngium maritimum* L.), a perennial of the Carrot family. A stiff, hairless but

spiny annual herb, completely iron-grey to bluish in colour, it grows to a height of 20 to 50 cm or more. The tiny flowers in dense flower-heads which bloom from June to August are also blue.

As opposed to the Sea Plantain, the Sea Holly grows exclusively on the sea coast. We can find it scattered on the Baltic and North Sea as well as in southern Europe and Asia Minor, on the Mediterranean Sea, the Atlantic ocean and Black Sea. In Britain it occurs on coasts as far north as Flamborough Head and on the west coast of Ireland.

Sea Holly grows in moving sands of flat coasts on sand dunes rich in nutrients. In these habitats it grows sporadically, in above-ground, sparse plant communities predominated by Sea Matroced (*Ammophila arenaria* (L.) Link.). Like Sea Holly, the entire community in most European countries is on the red lists marked as threatened. In some European countries, the Sea Holly is even protected by law.

In central Europe Sea Holly is a plant species which has been clearly indicated in the history of nature conservation. Its protection was declared relatively early on (Danzig 1902, 1920 all of Prussia at the same time, 1936 all Germany), and very soon it was motivated by ecological reasons: the enormous root system of these plants helps to reinforce mobile sand dunes and other sandbanks.

However, despite all the protection and care the Sea Holly has received, it is disappearing. Apart from the overall devastation caused by coastal recreational areas, urbanization and industrialization, it is also being greatly damaged by direct pursuit. It is an attractive and ornamental plant; moreover when dried it lasts for a very long time, so it belongs to the so-called immortals. Florists once picked it in abundance for markets, and holiday-makers like to pick it on the beaches as souvenirs of their summer holidays at the seaside.

The **Field Eryngo** (*Eryngium campestre* L.), a similar perennial with stems, leaves and flowers of pale greenish-white, is included in the British Red Data Book. This species is no halophyte but a plant which inhabits dry grassy places, usually however

◁ On many European beaches the thistle-like Sea Holly (*Eryngium maritimum*) is endangered or already extinct, having fallen victim to mass tourism and recreation.

▽ The Sea Kale (*Crambe maritima*) is not only a halophyte (salt-lover), but also thrives in nitrogen rich (nitrophilous) habitats: the fact that this species grows on sites with decaying seaweed, which most holiday-makers avoid, helps to protect it.

The Common Sea-lavender (*Limonium vulgare*), bril- ▷ liant with its densely clustered, straw-like flowers of a distinctive blue-violet colour at the end of summer in the grey-blue coastal salt meadows on the Baltic and North Sea. Unfortunately this sight is becoming more rare.

confined to a few locations on the coast in Devon, Hampshire, Kent and Guernsey. The two large Devon populations are well protected and said to be increasing.

A true halophyte of the sea coast is the legendary **Sea Kale** (*Crambe maritima* L.) of the Cress family. It is a stout, fleshy, hairless, blue, glaucous perennial with large lower pinnately lobed leaves, with a thickly branched stem up to 75 cm long. The tetramerous tiny flowers in the top racemes and panicles have white or pinkish petals and a pleasant honey scent. They blossom from the end of spring through the first half of the summer, from May to July.

Sea Kale is — with the exception of the Mediterranean Sea — a pioneer species in the saline swamps of European coastal sandbanks and at the edge of dunes. In central Europe it can be found occasionally on the Baltic coast from Schleswig-Holstein to Rügen. It is one of the main species there of the equally endangered pioneer community at the foot of cliffs — *Crambeetum maritimae*. It is also a characteristic species of plant communities — *Cakiletea maritimae* — on shingles washed down by the sea, often where there is a rich accumulation of seaweed humus. In Britain and Ireland it is more frequent along all coasts.

Sea Kale is an important honey and pollen-bearing plant and also provides fodder and oil for farming. In central Europe and other parts of the world it is traditionally cultivated as a vegetable. The pale early

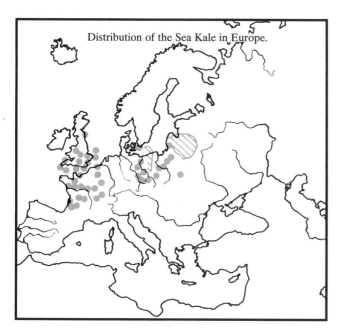

Distribution of the Sea Kale in Europe.

shoots (covered and therefore without green pigment) are prepared for eating in a similar way to asparagus. In Britain it was introduced into gardens two and half centuries ago from Devonshire. In some countries it is an officially protected species.

A charming flower of salty maritime meadows is the **Common Sea-lavender** (*Limonium vulgare* Mill.). The tiny lavender-lilac flowers of this perennial of the Thrift family are crowded into branched lax cymes. These grow to a height of 20 to 50 cm from a basal rosette of large tough, ovate elongated simple leaves. The plant flowers at the end of the summer — in August and September.

The occurrence of the Common Sea-lavender is restricted to the European sea coasts. In central Europe it is quite rare and can be found on muddy salt marshes on the North and Baltic Sea. These habitats, if not protected in reserves, are affected by various industrial activities and hence the Common Sea-lavender is disappearing. On the coasts of Britain the Common Sea-lavender is still quite common, often abundant as far north as Dumfries. Its dried inflorescence does not lose its shape or colour, so it is gathered a lot and used for winter bouquets. It is also sometimes cultivated as an ornamental plant.

Four other Sea-lavenders which are found in Britain are British Red Data Book species. **Matted Sea-lavender** (*Limonium bellidifolium* (Gouan) Dumort) is a tufted plant with oval leaves generally absent by flowering time (in summer). Flowers are small pale lilac panicles very much branched with numerous lower branches usually without flowers. This species grows all round the Mediterranean and in western Asia. In Britain it grows in drier parts of sandy salt-marshes in Norfolk and Lincolnshire; six localities are protected, two of them in National Nature Reserves. In Cam-

bridgeshire it has been extinct since the nineteenth century.

On the list of British protected plants, there are two rare species of the **Rock Sea-lavender** with violet-blue flowers slightly larger than those of the Common Sea-lavender. The species, both endemic to the British Isles, are: *Limonium recurvum* C. E. Salmon known to exist only in a single location on maritime rocks and cliffs in Dorset protected as a Site of Special Scientific Interest; and *Limonium paradoxum* Pugsl. existing in one UK location (also an SSSI) on basic igneous rocks on the Pembrokeshire coast, as well as in east Donegal.

Limonium transwallianum (Pugsl.) Pugsl. is also endemic to the British Isles, and is now probably confined to two localities with several hundreds of plants in the maritime cliffs of Pembrokeshire. The species is also known to exist in two places in Ireland.

The Bindweed genus of the Bindweed family (*Convolvulaceae*) is represented among the rare plant species on the sea coast by the attractive **Sea Bindweed** (*Convolvulus soldanella* L., syn. *Calystegia soldanella* (L.) R.Br.). As opposed to the more widespread and well known bindweeds, the herbaceous stem of this species is twining but prostrate and only 10 to 50 cm long. The alternate leaves are kidney-shaped, rather fleshy, long-stalked. The flowers are 3 to 5 cm long, pink with five white strips. This perennial flowers throughout the summer — from June to August.

The Sea Bindweed is a characteristic species of the community of coastal sands, dunes with predominating sand grasses — *Elymo-Ammophiletum*. It grows in places where this community is sparse. In ecological terms this plant is important for binding coastal sand dunes. It also has unusual geographical origins. Evidently it originally came from the Medi-

terranean, but it has spread or has been naturalized on beaches throughout the world, so that today it is considered a cosmopolitan species. In central Europe it rarely grows on the sand-dunes of North Sea islands. The first mention of it dates back to the 18th century. The Sea Bindweed occurs in southern Britain, but is rare in the north and apparently decreasing.

On the German red lists the Sea Bindweed is listed under the category of endangered and extinct species. It is one of the most endangered plants. It is damaged by recreational activity in its habitat and

because people pick it for its attractive flowers which blossom in the summer season. Some bindweeds are cultivated for ornamental flowers, resulting in many garden sorts. The conservation of the Sea Bindweed is therefore also important for the preservation of genetic resources which can be used in gardening. The heads and stalks were formerly gathered and dried for use as a medicinal drug.

Some species of the **Centauries** (*Centaurium*) of the Gentian family (*Gentianaceae*) rank among the ever more rare medicinal plants. Already the scientific name of the genus indicates the medicinal properties of the herb: it derives from the centaur Chiron who, according to ancient Greek mythology, had his injury cured by the centaury. The plant extracts, in particular magnesium, encourage the elimination of digestive juices and stimulate the appetite. It is found in two small representatives of the genus, near the sea, and the Lesser Centaury, growing on the maritime and inland salt-marshes of Europe. From the taxonomic/botanical point of view these species are rather complex. It is a rare protected plant which appears on red lists.

Seaside Centaury (*Centaurium littorale* (L.) Gilmour) is an annual or biennial herb, only 5 to 25 cm high and is bald or hairy with opposite mostly triple veined linear stem leaves. In the top cyme, when further developed it has elongated panicles, which blossom in the second half of the summer — from July to September — displaying tiny but ornamental pinkish-red five-petalled flowers. As is typical for halophytes, the leaves of this species tend to be somewhat fleshy.

Within its entire European range, the Seaside Centaury is considered a sub-Mediterranean, central European and oceanic species, occurring in two sub-species: *Centaurium littorale* (L.) Gilmour subsp.

littorale and the *Centaurium littorale* (L.) Gilmour subsp. *uliginosum* (W.et. Kit.) Rothm. ex Melderis. The first of these is a plant of maritime sandy and humous salt marshes. The second grows on lowland inland saline and wet meadows.

The more rare **Lesser Centaury** (*Centaurium pulchellum* (Sw.) Druce) can be found in similar habitats to the subspecies *uliginosum*. It tends to be even smaller than the Seaside Centaury (3 to 15 cm high), and is different because the lower part of the stem is richly branched and does not grow out of the basal rosette of leaves. The Lesser Centaury is a Eurasian-Mediterranean species. It is not such a strict halophyte as the Seaside Centaury. It is also found on fens and damp meadows, on clay or loam and gravel grounds rich in nutrients and more inland than on sea coasts from lowlands right up to uplands (over 800 m above sea level).

Both of these rare species of centaury are so small and inconspicuous that they can easily go unnoticed by experts as well as by laymen. However, their charm is obvious at a closer look. The natural habitats of these plants are disappearing fast due to waterworks and farming, so they should not be picked for use as medicinal plants. Nevertheless, their contents as already mentioned above make them a valuable genetic resource.

In the British Red Data Book there are three other centauries listed. The **Slender Centaury** (*Centaurium tenuiflorum* (Hoffmans. & Link) Fritsch) is similar to the Lesser Centaury but with stems only branched above the middle, branches rather erect,

flowers deep pink. This west European and Mediterranean species is found in damp grassy habitats, especially along the coast. It has been recorded in only two areas in England — in Dorset and the Isle of Wight; it also used to be found in the Channel Islands.

Perennial Centaury (*Centaurium scilloides* (L.f.) Samp.) is a short, spreading perennial with flowering and non-flowering shoots. Flowers are rather sparse, big (15—20 mm), pink, rarely white. It occurs on grassy cliffs in Cornwall, in the area which is protected as a Site of Special Scientific Interest.

The third British 'red' species **Broad-leaved Centaury** (*Centaurium latifolium* (Sm.) Druce), is an English endemic annual of dune slacks near Liverpool. Today it can be found only in herbariums: its extinction may have been caused by collectors.

A rather unattractive plant is the **Stalked Orache** (*Halimione pedunculata* (Grufb.) Aell). It is one of the plants of the Goosefoot or Fat Hen family (*Chenopodiaceae*), among all the oraches and goosefoots unfairly ignored by many nature lovers. Many members of this family are halophytes of maritime and inland saline habitats.

The Stalked Orache is found at both types of saline habitat. It is an annual, 10 to 40 cm high herb with an erect or ascendant almost round branched herbaceous stem which has ovate leaves; the upper leaves alternate and are shiny grey. The flowers are small, inconspicuous and grow in clusters; the fruit, in its shape, looks like a herbal fruit from a different family, the Shepherd's Purse. The Stalked Orache flowers from summer to autumn — from July to October.

This halophytic plant of western and northern European sea coasts and inland saline habitats from central parts of Germany through the Ukrainian and

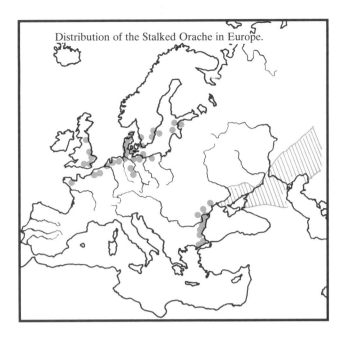
Distribution of the Stalked Orache in Europe.

official List of rare, endangered and endemic plant species in Europe. It always grows in the community of other significant halophytes such as Glasswort (*Salicornia europaea* L.), Annual Seablite (*Suaeda maritima* (L.) Dumort) and others. The conservation of this community will be possible only if entire biotopes are preserved by setting up protected territories with an organized system of care.

In Britain the species was first recorded in 1650. It occurred on the eastern shores of England in at least sixteen localities, but became extinct around 1935.

Perhaps the most well-known and important medicinal plant among the saline species is the robust **Marsh Mallow** (*Althaea officinalis* L.) indicated by its German folk name 'Heilwurzel' ('medical root'). The thicker roots are most widely picked, mainly in the autumn; however the dried flowers and leaves also provide the drug. All parts of the plant contain viscous properties which help clear the throat and ease inflammation of the mucous membrane. This herb is also recommended for treating inflammation of the urinary tract and intestinal difficulties, especially diarrhoea. The Marsh Mallow is cultivated as a medicinal plant in some cultures. It is now only rarely found growing in the wild, often in protected areas.

Russian steppes to Siberia is mostly declining in western and central Europe. It is a characteristic species of the fast disappearing grassy salt marshes. For example, on the German red list it is included as a highly threatened species and in France it is a species in danger of extinction. It is included in the

Distribution of the Bog Myrtle in Europe.

At first sight, the conspicuous feature of this tall (up to 1.5 metres), simple or slightly branched perennial herb is its thick silver-grey hairs which even cover some parts of the flowers. The large flowers (up to 5 cm on average) in sparse racemes reveal that the plant belongs to the Mallow family (*Malvaceae*). The corollas of the flowers are violet or pinkish white with a silky sheen. It flowers from July to September.

Geographically, the Marsh Mallow is a Mediterranean-continental species extending from Europe to central Asia. The specimens found in central Europe, particularly in coastal bushes, on damp meadows and pastures, are naturalized. The only native habitats are in damp, salt and brackish marshes rich in nutrients, pastures, reeds and ditches and, relatively rarely, in inland salines. In Britain the Marsh Mallow is a local coastal species in England south of the Wash and in South Wales. Further north there are only scattered colonies. It also occurs rarely in south-west Ireland.

The British Red Data Book includes the **Rough Marsh Mallow** (*Althaea hirsuta* L.). A short to medium sized annual or biennial with pinkish-lilac flowers, it occurs on dry soils in field borders, scrub and woodland margin, but not on the sea coast. It is native probably only in Somerset and in Kent.

The only woody plant dealt with in this chapter is the **Bog Myrtle** or **Sweet Gale** (*Myrica gale* L.) of the Bog Myrtle family (*Myricaceae*), which resembles willows. It must have already been known in ancient times because its old common name 'gagel', in the form 'gagol', is found in the old Anglo-Saxon language. It is not a halophyte but a species widely spread across the peat-bogs from south-western Europe to the St Petersburg region; it can also be found in North America. In central Europe it has a so-called Atlantic character, i.e. the plant is found in the zone directly next to the sea coast. It also grows on peat-bogs which are sometimes flooded by sea water. In Britain it inhabits bogs and heaths mainly in the north and west. Scattered localities are in Cornwall, southern England and East Anglia.

The Bog Myrtle is not a tall shrub, growing only to about 1.5 metres in height, and it looks very much like a small willow. It has lanceolate, blue-grey green leaves which are toothed at the top. The inflorescences — catkins — appear in early spring, normally in April: the females are shorter than the males.

The plant is conspicuous for its strong aromatic scent. Its leaves were therefore used against various unwelcome insects in households, especially wardrobe moths. Sometimes they were added to beer as a substitute for hops. In Norway the thinly sliced dried leaves were mixed into tobacco. Even today the properties of this plant are interesting from the point of view of pharmaceuticals and chemistry and so the specimens of the species are a precious natural genetic resource which deserves protection.

In most countries on the Baltic coast the Bog Myrtle is regarded as an endangered species although it is not listed under the priority threat categories. On peat-bogs and in the *Myricetum* community it is found with other threatened species, for example some hydrophilous sedges (*Carex*). In some areas in Britain (e.g. Shropshire) the occurrence of this threatened species is decreasing rapidly.

FRESHWATERS

Every open water surface in European conditions is, sooner or later, colonized by plants, some of which are rare and in need of protection.

There are thousands of bodies of water throughout the European countryside: lakes formed during the ice age in northern Europe, large lakes at the foot of the Alps, small tarns in the mountains, fish-ponds representing water management of past centuries and large lake dams as their contemporary equivalent. Small and large ribbons of water courses have meandered unless their pace and direction have been forced by man in straight canals; however, in some places the branches and pools of such rivers survive.

In the temperate zone of Europe, in its unique biome of broad-leaf and mixed forests, there is a natural trend in the development of vegetation towards the forest. Each place, exposed in some way, is immediately colonized with plants. Firstly, the individual pioneer species appear to create the pioneer communities. Through a series of ever more complicated plant communities, so-called succession, development culminates in the top community, in our conditions normally the forest community. Neither still nor flowing waters escape the onset of vegetation. The leafless and leafy green herbaceous stems of the plants thrive under the surface, large green leaves and coloured flowers intermingle at the surface or even entire inflorescences protrude from the water. These tend to be conspicuous, beautiful and interesting plants.

Most of the plant communities of submerged or floating vegetation of European waters are now among the most threatened plant communities. Human activity disturbs the water biotopes: various waste, sewage from the local farm land and direct effects of fisheries (fertilization of fishponds, feeding of fish) is altering the quality of the water. Most of them are over-saturated with nutrients so that many large and conspicuous aquatic plants, so-called mac-

rophytes, are disappearing. The once crystal clear lakes with underwater 'meadows' of *Charophyceae* — algae resembling horsetails in both appearance and size — are badly affected.

The variety of water vegetation can only be preserved in its entirety by a system of protected territories with secured care. For visitors to these territories the standard conservation rules apply in the sense of 'Do not pick, do not pull up, do not trample'. However, the public can do a lot more today to contribute towards the conservation of threatened aquatic plants, for example by protecting a pool with water-lilies from being covered up or campaigning against the drainage of sewage into a water-lily pond.

Not many people know that some ferns also belong to aquatic plants. Many species of the Salvinia family (*Salviniaceae*) float on the surface. Their European representative is **Salvinia** (*Salvinia natans* (L.) All.). It is one of the most handsome, best-known and also most endangered of the water ferns. Together with some exotic species of the Salvinia family, it is cultivated as an aquarium plant.

The Salvinia is an annual rootless fern. The long (up to 20 cm) herbaceous stem floats freely on the water. It has groups of three leaves in whorls. The upper two leaves are about 1 cm long of a roughly ovate shape floating on the surface. On the green upper side they have hairy tufts to prevent them from getting wet. The third lower leaf of the whorl is submerged and is divided into about a dozen filamentary segments which resemble roots. These carry rounded spore-cases.

The overall geographical range of the species is Eurasian-continental. The border of it runs across the western parts of central Europe, thus it is not native in Britain. The habitats of these ferns are still or slowly flowing waters warmed by the sun, protected

◁ Even open water surfaces carry flowering plants: in the picture a white Water Crowfoot, popularly known as 'water-sprite's hair'.

The Salvinia (*Salvinia natans*) is an annual rootless ▷ fern. On the upper side of the floating leaves it has ▽ bunches of hairs which prevent them from getting wet.

The Frogbit (*Hydrocharis morsus-ranae*) has large male ▷ flowers with 12 stamens on long thin stalks in a spathe of two thin bracts.

The Yellow Water-lily (*Nuphar lutea*) is a quite wide-▷ ▽ spread aquatic plant living not only in acid, nutritionally poor waters, but also in water courses and reservoirs which are rich in nutrients and even slightly polluted.

against the wind and often bordered by bushes or forests. The Salvinia grows closer to the banks and sometimes infiltrates the reeds on the banks. In central Europe it is a rare species in the upper Rhineland, in the river basins of the Main, the Elbe, the Havel, the Spree and the Oder, in the Austrian, Czech and Slovak and Hungarian Morava and Danubian river basins. In the river springs and pools, naturally rich in nutrients (eutrophic), it is found with several species of Duckweed (*Lemna*). The *Spirodelo-Salvinietum* plant community, characteristic for its occurrence of Salvinia, is one of the most threatened of European communities.

The only native small water fern of Britain is the **Pillwort** (*Pilulavia glubulifera* L.) from the Pillwort family (*Marsiliaceae*). This is a submerged, not floating plant with filiform bright green fronds, the fertile ones bearing globular utricles like little pills. Once widespread in Great Britain (much more restricted in Ireland) it has declined considerably due to the filling of ponds and drainage.

The **Frogbit** (*Hydrocharis morsus-ranae* L.) of the Frogbit family (*Hydrocharitaceae*) has similar demands on the environment to the Salvinia. The well-known Canadian Pondweed (*Elodea canadensis* Michx), also belongs to the same family. This aquarium plant, introduced from the North American continent to the European countryside in 1840, was the scourge of waters for a certain time, but is now also on the decline.

The Frogbit is a robust, 15 to 30 cm high herb, floating on the water surface. It spreads out its long-stalked green leaves with kidney- or heart-shaped leathery blades formed into a rosette. The flowers protrude from the water surface, the females are large, on average about 3 cm with 3 orbicular white petals and 12 stamens. It blossoms from June to August.

The floating Frogbit belongs in duck-weed communities which form floating blankets on water surfaces. It occurs in waters which are stagnant or slow flowing, protected against the wind, warm in the summer, slightly shadowed, rich in nutrients — most often in shallow pools, concealed arms of water courses and sheltered lake bays, mainly in shallow places. Sometimes it can be found among sparse coastal reed.

Once the Frogbit was quite common in Euro-Siberian waters. With changes to and disappearance of water biotopes, it is becoming a rarity in central Europe. It appears that the only reliable sanctuary will remain well-managed protected territories. In Britain the plant used to be common (not indigenous in Scotland). It is decreasing now due to agricultural developments.

One of the largest plants of open waters is the **Yellow Water-lily** (*Nuphar lutea* (L.) Smith) of the Water-lily family (*Nymphaceae*). This stout plant, growing in the mud on the bottom, has a thick (up to 10 cm) creeping rhizome which bears long, stalked leaves and single flowers on long scapes; depending on the depth of the water on the site, the scapes can be up to 2.5 metres high. The leaf blades float on the surface, are entire, broadly ovate and deeply cleft to the stalk, 12—30 cm long, leathery with nerves on the end, furcate and not interwoven. The flowers with a yellow corolla measure 4 to 6 cm on average; they bloom from June to August and protrude slightly out of the water surface. They give off an intense, pleasant scent resembling apple. The fruit — flashy capsules 3 — 4 cm in length — float on the surface because they contain air follicles in their webs. They can be carried away by water currents and when the follicles collapse, they drop to the bottom.

Formerly the Yellow Water-lily was widespread throughout Europe and Siberia. It is gathered as a medicinal plant and this sometimes led to the diminishment and perhaps extinction of the populations. It is also cultivated as an ornamental aquatic plant so it was transported to some localities when a pond was planted for decoration. In its rhizome particularly it contains starch with alkaloids which have not yet been fully examined. The drug from the rhizome is added as a sedative to special preparations used for nervous disorders and excessive irritation.

The canalization of water courses, drainage and filling of concealed arms and pools is leading, in some regions of Europe, to a decline in the Yellow Water-lily. It has appeared on the lists of protected plant species of several central European states (Germany, Switzerland, the Czech and Slovak Republics) because people also pick it for its attractive flowers and gather the rhizomes. However, this plant has rather broad ecological complitude, as has been discovered lately, and it withstands strong eutrophication of waters and, to a certain degree, pollution

— so it is not usually considered a too threatened species.

Much more rare, threatened and strictly protected in central Europe is the **Least Water-lily** (*Nuphar pumila* (L.) DC.). This northern species has been preserved as a glacial relict in central Europe. In Britain it occurs only rarely in Wales and in the Scottish Highlands. The only English locality where it is found is in Shropshire where — as an endangered plant — it has become the emblem of the Shropshire Conservation Trust. It is more sensitive than the Yellow Water-lily; above all it requires clean oligotro-

Distribution of the White Water-lily in Europe.

▽ The White Water-lily (*Nymphaea alba*) has very attractive, shiny, white flowers: they are the largest flowers in European flora.

The Fringed Water-lily (*Nymphoides peltata*), the smal- ▷ lest of the 'water-lilies', has rich golden-yellow petals with a fringed margin.

The Water Chestnut (*Trapa natans*) spreads long- ▷ ▽ stalked leaves with rhombic blades across the water surface. Its native occurrence in some European locations is disputable today.

One of the numerous fish ponds in the Třeboň basin in Bohemia, which is a Biosphere Reserve, was dug up several years ago because tall sedges were spreading and creating a swamp. This intervention meant disturbance of the natural development of vegetation but it brought a surprising result: a strong colony of rare water-lilies appeared in the fishpond.

White Water-lilies are often included in the lists of officially protected and threatened plant species throughout Europe. They are undoubtedly one of the most ornamental plants with the largest (up to 12 cm on average) flowers made up of a large number of shiny white petals. The flowers bloom from June to August and open only during daylight hours. The large leathery leaf blades on long leaf stalks float along the surface (we distinguish them from the leaves of the Yellow Water-lily by the furcate veins joining at the end). The arrangement of the main nerves on the leaves is one of the distinguishing features of the two European species of White Water-lily. In the **White Water-lily** (*Nymphaea alba* L.), with large flowers, its main nerves are almost straight, in the *Nymphaea candida* J.S. et K.B. Presl with smaller flowers, they are distinctly bent into an arch. The

phic waters in, for instance, lowland pools and mountain lakes. Both water-lilies are found in the plant communities with floating species from the water-lily family and with submerged and floating representatives of water-milfoils and hornworts.

In fishponds submerged and floating vegetation is artificially removed. In protecting space for their fish fishermen are preventing the growth of plants and gradual silting up. Nature protectionists used to fight against this because they considered this intervention to be a danger to the existence of some aquatic plants, particularly the conspicuous water-lilies. Today, however, it is becoming clear that careful intervention is proving to be beneficial and is also part of the management of fresh water reserves.

latter species is rarer. The north-western border of its geographical range runs across Germany.

The White Water-lily contains valuable matter, particularly in its thick creeping rhizome. It was used in the tanning industry for its content of tannic acids. Today great attention is paid to investigating the alkaloids which suppress the growth of tumorous cells. As a medicinal plant White Water-lily is added to special preparations used for nervous disorders. The alkaloids contained in the water-lily are slightly poisonous.

The White Water-lily is understandably also a popular ornamental water flower. It is planted not only in ponds and garden pools, but also in wider expanses of water, such as fishponds in parks. Hence it is sometimes difficult to decide which locality is its indigenous one. The conservation of the White Water-lily is an important species in terms of genetic resources. It is endangered by water management works which destroy its biotopes and by water pollution to which it has a lower tolerance than the related Yellow Water-lily. Also the excessive development of recreation areas destroys it.

In European water-lily pads there also grows the yellow-flowering **Fringed Water-lily** (*Nymphoides peltata* (S.G. Gmel) Kuntze). As its generic name indicates, its appearance resembles the water-lilies, but the 5-part flowers, in average measuring about 3 cm, with fringed lobes of a funnel-shaped corolla, show it to be one of the Gentian family. This perennial herb, with long rhizomes, has a rounded stem and long-stalked rounded leaves. It flowers from July to September.

The Eurasian species occurs throughout Europe in waters of 0.5 — 1.5 m depth, mainly in slow flowing or still waters which are naturally supplied with nutrients. It grows well in areas with a warm summer

and mild winter. As a consequence of direct and indirect destruction of suitable biotopes, it has become a rarity in central Europe. It has survived in a number of protected territories and is often the main or one of the main reasons for their establishment.

In Britain the Fringed Water-lily occurs locally in eastern, central and south-east England as far north as southern Yorkshire. It is widely cultivated and in some areas (also in Scotland and Ireland) is naturalized in nutrient-rich pools and canals.

Sometimes one comes across a strange thing growing in the water. Some sort of woody nut with thorny horns. In some fishpond districts it was once picked for making into necklaces and other ornaments. The seed contains starch (up to 52%), albumen and oil. In lake districts it was used for food and it is still eaten in the Far East. It is the fruit of the aquatic **Water Chestnut** (*Trapa natans* L.), the only representative of its genus from the Water Chestnut family (*Trapaceae*).

The nut drops to the bottom, germinates and roots an annual herb which grows from it. Like the nut, the

entire plant is angular and horny. Thanks to the swollen stalks, functioning like floating follicles, the leaves with rhombic, sharp toothy blades float on the water surface. They form a rosette which is also angular and rhombic in shape. Branched, thread-like green roots grow on the submerged stem. The white 4-part flowers in the rosette of leaves are inconspicuous and bloom from June to September.

The Water Chestnut also belongs to the aquatic plant community called the pads. This Eurasian species grows in lowland, quiet, still waters at a depth of 1 to 2 m. Formerly the Water Chestnut was much more widespread in Europe, as palaeobotanical and archaeological findings from the later stone age period show. To a certain extent, it was formerly a semi-cultural or even cultural plant and as a consequence of this it was usually artificially spread. Today due to man's intervention in marshlands, the Water Chestnut is on the decline. It is on the List of rare, endangered and endemic plants of Europe. The Water Chestnut is not native in Britain.

While the flowers of all the aquatic plants described so far tend to grow close to the water surface, the **Water Violet** (*Hottonia palustris* L.) has a whorled raceme of white or pinkish flowers which grow to a height of over 25 cm directly above the water surface. The flowers, blooming from May to June, are 5-part, quite large (about 2 cm in diameter) and attractive. The shape of these flowers indicates

◁ The Water Violet (*Hottonia palustris*) holds its whorled racemes of decorative white or pinkish flowers high above the water surface; the stems are covered by glandular hairs.

▽ In Europe today the Water Lobelia (*Lobeliu dortman na*) is a very rare plant found in clean lakes which are low in nutrients. A long stem with a lax raceme of pale violet flowers rises above the shallow waters.

The Water Soldier (*Stratiotes aloides*) with its tough ▷ sword-like leaves resembles the Desert Aloe. It is an aquatic plant, its floating, partially submerged leafy rosettes creating rare 'aquatic meadows' on some waters.

At first sight, the Bladderworts (*Utricularia*) closely re- ▷ ▽ semble one another: the attractive two-lipped pale to dark yellow flowers rise above the water surface.

that this perennial belongs to the Primrose family (*Primulaceae*). The deeply pinnatifid leaves with narrow-linear lobes arranged into a rosette, do not float on the surface but are mostly submerged.

The Water Violet is a European species. It is found in smaller lowland pools, concealed river branches, ditches or other shallow waters rich in nutrients. It forms the submerged pads of the plant community called Water Violet, which is one of those plant communities that are disappearing. The Water Violet is often abundant in places where it does occur, but it is quite rare and if we take into account the overall threat to the freshwater biotopes, then it needs to be protected. In Britain the Water Violet is localised in lowland England, scarce in Wales and Ireland and is not found in Scotland.

One of the rarest European waterplants is the **Water Lobelia** (*Lobelia dortmanna* L.). Very few people would expect an

aquatic plant in the herb family to belong to popular, traditionally cultivated garden flowers. It belongs to the Lobelia family (*Lobeliaceae*), divided some time ago from the Bellflower family (*Campanulaceae*) from which it differs in its irregular flowers.

The Water Lobelia is a perennial herb growing to about half a metre tall. The white to bluish pale violet flowers bloom in July and August in a sparse elongated raceme protruding high above shallow water in which its thick ground rosette of fresh green linear leaves is submerged. The plant is poisonous.

Today the Water Lobelia is only rarely found in the temperate zone of western, central and northern Europe and in North America. It grows near the coast, within reach of the damp maritime area. Its habitats are flat, sandy oligotrophic (poor in nutrients) banks of slightly acid lakes with a depth of 10 to 30 m. As already mentioned, it is these biotopes which are the most affected and damaged by human activities. In eastern Germany the Water Lobelia is extinct. In western Germany it is in danger of extinction and was declared a protected species. Likewise elsewhere (e.g. in the former USSR), the realization that there are only a few representatives of this species left has motivated the declaration of protected territories. In Britain, the Water Lobelia is found in Wales, the Lake District, Scotland and West Ireland. In some regions (e.g. in Shropshire) it has not been seen for many years and is considered to have become a victim of eutrophication.

The **Heath Lobelia** (*Lobelia urens* L.) is included in the British Red Data Book. This is a medium sized erect perennial with leafy stems and blue or purplish flowers in lax spike-like racemes. This attractive plant grows in damp habitats (pastures, heaths, woodland margins), but not in open waters. It is very vulnerable to grazing by cattle, and particularly sus-

ceptible to being swamped by coarser vegetation, especially bracken. It is known to exist in about 10 localities in Cornwall, Devon, Dorset, Hampshire and Sussex, and is extinct in Kent and Herefordshire.

One of the submerged aquatic plants growing in open freshwaters throughout the world is the interesting **Bladderwort** (*Utricularia*) belonging to the relatively small Butterwort family (*Lentibulariaceae*). The herbaceous stems of the bladderworts do not root in the bottom, but float freely in the water. Their leaves have two types of lobes: thin, thread-like, and follicular hollow and swollen. The herbaceous stems of the bladderworts can be over a metre long. The lemon yellow to orange attractive 2-lipped flowers protrude from the surface most often in sparse racemes. They are about 2 cm in size and bloom through the summer — from June to September. The bladderworts are perennial plants.

The bladderworts are of interest to biologists as they are carnivorous. The trapping and digestive mechanism are 1 to 5 mm long sac-like bladders which are one of the most interesting creations of the plant kingdom. It is a miniature trap equipped with a type of 'trap door'. Inside there is an area of low pressure. When some tiny crustacean or other water animal touches the closure of the aperture 'the trap door' opens and the low pressure sucks the victim into the bladder. The trapped animal is digested in-

Distribution of the Quillwort *Isoetes lacustris* in Europe.

The Quillwort *Isoetes lacustris* is an aquatic stemless cryptogam, an extremely rare plant which grows on the bottom of clean, nutrient-poor lakes: such habitats have been rapidly declining in recent years in Europe.

side the bladder by enzymes secreted by a special type of gland, which breaks up albuminous matter.

There are several different species of bladderworts in Europe which only an expert can distinguish. They differ in small morphological features and in their environmental requirements. They are found in still or flowing water from 5 cm to more than 3 m deep, with varying amounts of nutrients. The **Greater Bladderwort** (*Utricularia vulgaris* L.) has equally shaped leaves, with 20 to 200 bladders almost half a centimetre long. The pale yellow *Utricularia australis* R. B. R. has fewer bladders (8–75), which are smaller in size (up to 3 mm). The other species have no more than 10 bladders. The *Utricularia bremii* Heer and the *Utricularia ochroleuca* Hartm. grow in pools and depressions of limeless peat-bogs which are poor in nutrients. The **Lesser Bladderwort** (*Utricularia minor* L.) grows in similar habitats but ones which are richer in nutrients and often contain lime. The bladderworts are not as yet found on the lists of officially protected species in Europe, but in view of the rapid destruction of water biotopes, all the species are listed in various threat categories on central European red lists.

The British flora numbers some five bladderwort species. Perhaps the Lesser Bladderwort is the most widespread one; others are localized or rare. Many once-recorded sites of occurrence have been lost through changes in land use and drainage.

An interesting and endangered plant community of warm European waters is 'water meadows' where the **Water Soldier** (*Stratiotes aloides* L.) predominates. This plant is one of the already mentioned Frogbit family (*Hydrocharitaceae*). It is notable particularly for its funnel-shaped rosettes of tough, sword-like, serrate toothy leaves with pointed ends, resembling semi-desert and cultivated aloe or a

pineapple top. The rosette of leaves is 15 to 40 cm tall, floating on the surface or submerged underneath it. In places this protruding perennial forms entire thick 'lawns'. The white 3-part flowers, measuring 3 to 4 cm in diameter, bloom from June to August.

The Water Soldier, named after its sword-like foliage, is the only species of this genus. It is found in Europe and Siberia in still and slow flowing lime-free waters which are rich in nutrients. It occurs there at a depth of 0.5 to 2 metres. In dried out pools it is able to last up to five years in a latent state, but it cannot survive the drying up of entire river branches and similar waters which are its natural habitats (it has been planted in some European localities). So the Water Soldier is disappearing in Europe and is found on red lists and on lists of plant species protected by law.

In Britain, it is found in stations scattered throughout the country. In western England it is rare, and in Ireland and Scotland it is naturalized. Also the plant was introduced to some English regions and is well established in shallow pools.

Finally, there is one rarity which belongs to cryptogams. On the bed of clean tarns which are low in nutrients, at a depth of up to 8 m, we sometimes

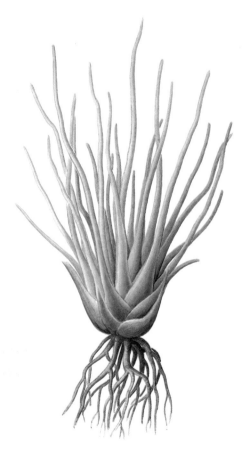

find 'meadows' of strange grassy plants. They are composed of a rosette of long, semirounded green leaves. They grow from short rhizomes and at the base they have swollen sheaths which enclose spore-cases. These non-flowering, sporophytic perennial plants belong to the *Isoetes* genus of the Quillwort family — the *Isoetaceae.*

The European Quillwort species, *Isoetes lacustris* L. and *Isoetes echinospora* Durieu, grow to about 20 cm in height. Both can still be found in the foot-hills of the Alps, the Vosges, the Black Forest, the Bohemian Forest and the Karkonosze (Giant Mountains) in Poland. Formerly they were found in the lakes of the central European lowlands. In Britain only the first species occurs in mountainous parts of Scotland, northern England and Wales, many of the previously recorded sites of occurrence now being reported as missing or extinct. Of course it is difficult to prove the occurrence of these remarkable plants. This is possible if the leaves or entire rosettes become detached from the bottom and are carried to the water surface or washed up onto the bank.

The Quillworts require a great deal of protection, especially territorial protection of entire biotopes. Several species included on the European red list grow in southern Europe. In northern Italy there is the *Isoetes malinverniana* Ces. et De Not.

The **Land Quillwort** (*Isoetes histrix* Bory) is included in the British Red Data Book. As its name indicates, it is a terrestrial species of moist maritime turf which grows in at least 14 colonies in Cornwall. There are other colonies in the Channel Islands. One is protected in a National Nature Reserve, six are in Sites of Special Scientific Interest.

SHALLOW WETLANDS, WATER BANKS, RIVERINE FORESTS

Wetlands — shallow water reservoirs with swampy borders — are biotopes inhabited by a tremendous wealth of species, but are among those habitats which are most endangered throughout Europe.

The plants discussed in the previous chapter form the basis of aquatic plant growth. In this chapter we will focus on some other water area species which are also in need of conservation. These are plants which grow on banks or shallow marshes and also in woods alongside water courses.

Inland marshes are one of the most endangered biotopes in Europe today. Many diverse natural areas which link open waters — on the bank — riverine forests — have suffered as a consequence of the development of the Rhineland, the Elbe basin, the Danubian basin and the smaller European courses. Rivers have been shortened, straightened, their inlets, dead arms and pools, often resembling tropical jungles, have been drained, changed into meadows and fields or built up. Felled woods have been replaced with agriculture, housing estates, industrial enterprises and various roads and communications. Furthermore, water is constantly being polluted and this, of course, affects the vegetation in the water and on the banks particularly certain sensitive species. The Rhine has become a sewer throughout almost its entire course.

In recent years the construction of waterworks on European rivers has greatly affected the situation with regard to lowland grasslands and the precious remaining alluvial woodlands. One might recall the struggle of the Austrian nature conservationists against the construction of the dam at Hainburg. It is there along the Danubian tributary, the Morava river, and its tributary the Thaya (Dyje) river, despite various waterwork activities in the past (but in some cases also thanks to them), that this remarkable world has been preserved. A world of slowly flowing waters and woods with concealed branches and pools: a world of diverse spring flowers and summer nettle and bush-rope jungle; a world of water birds

and aquatic plants; one of the last great natural paradises of central Europe. The bilateral Biosphere Reserve created by means of Czecho-Slovak-Austrian cooperation should, in the near future, connect the existing smaller protected territories and preserve the unique ecosystems with their wealth of species.

Similar international cooperation already exists between Austria and Hungary in another marsh paradise on the largest steppe lake in central Europe. It is the bilateral Biosphere Reserve of the Neusiedler Lake (Fortö-tö in Hungarian).

Lakes of glacial origin in northern Europe, in Britain or at the foothills of the Alps are also bordered by interesting shore vegetation although the plants are often on the decline or are changing as a result of the excess nutrients (eutrophication) found in the lakes, the intensive recreation or other causes. Sometimes shore and marsh vegetation continues to grow in protected areas. In Britain such a wetland paradise is the Broads National Park with its 28,800 hectares, established in eastern England in 1989.

Central European fishponds represent interesting ecosystems although they were artificially created by human activity. In many places in Europe, the traditional fishpond districts have become a model for the ecological creation of the countryside. A well-known example is the Biosphere Reserve — the Protected Landscape Area Třeboň Region in south Bohemia.

Is the development of vegetation in European waters restricted for good, can we now only count the losses and guard or maybe cultivate the remaining rare plants in the protected territories? This certainly does not have to be the case. New dams are not just to be considered as destructive to nature and the countryside, but should also be thought of as a new

◁ The Bog Arum (*Calla palustris*) resembles the tropical and glasshouse Calla: its flowers are tiny and the conspicuous part of the inflorescence is the white spathe — the bract enfolding a spadix of flowers.

▽ An interesting type of wetland found in the European countryside and important for preserving a wealth of species, although it is basically a human creation, is the artificial fish pond.

The Great Fen-sedge (*Cladium mariscus*) of the ▷ Sedge family (*Cyperaceae*) is a rare grass-like marsh herb. Its hibernating leaves have very rough sharp edges resembling a small saw.

opportunity for the growth of aquatic plants. The rational utilization of the countryside is leading to the construction of new water reservoirs, not so much for fishing purposes as for water management and ecological reasons. Derelict gravel pits are flooded with water which is usually surprisingly clean and within a few years botanists are recording new findings there. Sometimes suitable places can be discovered in these new terrains — substitute habitats where it is possible to transfer critically endangered plants, thereby preserving them not in an artificial seed or tissue gene bank but in the open countryside with the continuation of all economic, ecological, scientific-cultural and aesthetic functions of the plant species in question.

A large number of the habitats included in this chapter (and in the subsequent two chapters) are in-

habited by **Bog Arum** (*Calla palustris* L.). This is a remarkable perennial of the Arum family (*Araceae*) which is particularly widespread in the tropics. Some of them are favourite house plants in Europe or are cultivated in glass-houses for cutting. The so-called Calla (the correct botanical genus is *Zantedeschia*) is a favourite flower for wedding bouquets.

The Bog Arum in its appearance, particularly the flowers — or the inflorescence — resembles its relation. In the open countryside it looks exotic due to the fact that marshy woods are often compared to tropical swamp jungles. It is a herb 15 to 30 cm high with a green cylindrical segmented rhizome. The leaves are long-stalked with orbicular heart-shaped blades, light to dark green in colour, smooth, shiny and leathery. The inflorescence is composed of many tiny flowers formed in a cylindrical spadix which is wrapped inside into a clean white opened spathe, 6 to 7 cm in length. The plant flowers from late spring to early autumn — from May to September — and is pollinated by insects and slugs. The fruit is a red berry.

The German name Schlangenwurzel (i.e. snake root) is derived from the snake-like appearance of

Distribution of the Great Fen-sedge in Europe.

the rhizome and this led people to believe that it might have curative effects against snake bites. The whole plant contains the aroid alkaloid and is poisonous. Due to its ornamental look, people sometimes pull up and replant the Bog Arum in gardens or around fish ponds. So it is difficult to know where this plant is indigenous. For example, in Switzerland the protected Bog Arum is only native in one site. In Britain the Bog Arum is not native at all: it has been introduced and naturalized in certain areas (for example in Shropshire and Surrey).

The habitats of Bog Arum are very wet, permanently or occasionally flooded places. It is found near slowly flowing waters, in ditches with pools, on the shores of shallow lakes and fish ponds, among tall sedges in alder bushes and forests or in peat-bogs. It grows from the lowlands (in relative abundance in the northern part of central Europe) up to highlands (in the Bohemian Forest, Bavaria, it is found, for instance, in Arber Tarn). It is protected by official decree in Belgium, France, Austria, Germany and the Czech Republic. Bog Arum is a circumpolar species; therefore it is found mostly in northern Europe.

Some plants which are typical of very wet, lake and riverside and swampy habitats are the members of the Sedge family (*Cyperaceae*). Various sedges (*Carex*) belong to this family, creating a diverse community in the marshes. These are rather difficult plants for a layperson to identify and they are easy to confuse. However, the **Great Fen-sedge** (*Cladium mariscus*) (L.) Pohl) is a distinctive sight among the *Cyperaceae*. It is a robust (up to 2 m high), perennial, grass-like herb. As its name indicates in most European languages, it has characteristic sharp toothy keeled ribs of grey-green, with leaves about 1.5 cm wide. The brown flower spikelets are drawn into an elongated panicle at the end of a blunt, three-sided

herbaceous stem. The plant flowers in June and July.

Although the Great Fen-sedge is broadly believed to be a cosmopolitan species in view of its widespread occurrence, today it is a rare plant in central Europe, on the decline and listed as a threatened species in the German red list and endangered in the Czech and Slovak Republics. It is most likely to be found in lake areas in northern central Europe. A significant pioneer plant growing by lakes, pools and ditches and a member of today's endangered community in Europe is the *Cladietum*. It is a calcicolous plant growing on ground which often contains a considerable amount of carbonates. The best guarantee for the conservation of this interesting member of the European flora is the creation of well-managed protected territories. In Britain the Great Fen-sedge is sparsely scattered over England, common in the west of Ireland, and very rare in Scotland.

A common plant growing on riverbanks in the lowlands of Europe is the **Flowering Rush** (*Butomus umbellatus* L.). Its is an attractive herb belonging to the Flowering Rush family (*Butomaceae*) of monocotyledons. With leaves (7 to 12 in ground rosettes) which look like reeds, this stout perennial resembles some sort of grass, until its bright, decorative umbellate inflorescence appears. This inflorescence has 15 to 30 3-part flowers with pink, dark red veined corollas on a rounded, unbranched scape. The flowers blossom from June to September.

The strong horizontal rhizome of the Flowering Rush roots mainly under water at the shore of flowing and stagnant waters, in small pools and ditches in the middle of wetland and meadows. It is a plant which requires a lot of nutrients and it is thermophilic. It often grows as a pioneer species between the taller wetland herbs. It can also withstand the considerable differences of the water surface. It is scattered in the lowlands and hills of Europe and Asia.

The Flowering Rush is a suitable plant for growing on the banks of reservoirs and is also cultivated in gardens and parks. In Europe it is now relatively rare. In the Netherlands and some Swiss cantons it is an officially protected species. In Britain the Flowering Rush is reasonably widespread (rare in Wales only), but decreasing recently.

A rare plant found in the wet habitats of lowland meadows alongside large European rivers is the **Gratiole** (*Gratiola officinalis* L.) of the Figwort family (*Scrophulariaceae*). This perennial, hairless herb grows to a height of 40 cm. The hollow direct or ascendant stems with opposite sessile leaves carry in the axil of the upper leaves single, long-stalked flowers about 1 cm long. It has white, red veined or tinged 2-lipped corollas. The Gratiole flowers from June to August.

As its specific name indicates, the creeping segmented rhizome and the stalk of the Gratiole was once picked and used in folk medicine. The herb is rich in various glycosides related to the glycosides of the foxglove. However, it is highly poisonous and therefore when it was used internally in the past there were cases of poisoning. It was also believed that children were poisoned after drinking cow's milk from cows which grazed on a large amount of Gratiole. The stalk brew was used for malaria, constipation, liver diseases, gonorrhoea and intestinal parasites. Both the brew and powder from the dried herb were recommended for various disorders, including

melancholy and delirium tremens. The leaves were applied externally to wounds, ulcers and rashes.

Today the Gratiole is no longer included among medicinal plants according to the official pharmacopoeia. Nevertheless, it represents a valuable genetic resource which should be preserved in the countryside. Today's gatherers of medicinal plants would have problems finding it because it has become a rarity. It appears on red lists, in Germany it has even been on the list of officially protected plant species. It is found in the temperate, more northern zones of Europe and western Asia. In central Europe it grows on wet, occasionally or permanently flooded places in the lowland meadows of the Rhine, Danube, Elbe, Oder and several other rivers. Its occurrence in several protected nature territories should guarantee the preservation of the species. The Gratiole is not found in the UK.

Among the water, shore and bog plants are representatives of the Buttercup family (*Ranunculaceae*), particularly *Ranunculus* genus and the closely related *Batrachium* genus. An attractive plant which grows in water margin reed and sedge communities is the robust **Great Spearwort** (*Ranunculus lingua* L.). It is a perennial herb which grows to a height of 0.5–1 m. Erect stems with few upper branches grow from a hollow rhizome. The leaves are almost grass-like, narrowly lanceolate, flat with almost parallel veins. The large golden-yellow flowers (2–4 cm in diameter), which have a greasy, shiny appearance, bloom from May to August.

Like other species of this family, the Great Spearwort has much interesting matter which is the subject of research. Some of this is slightly poisonous. It is being cultivated more and more as an ornamental flower in the vicinity of larger reservoirs.

Great Spearwort grows throughout Europe and

△ The Gratiole (*Gratiola officinalis*) has long thin stalks and a long corolla tube of solitary flowers.

△ The Flowering Rush (*Butomus umbellatus*) with its decorative umbel of four-part flowers once grew abundantly on water banks; today it is becoming a rarity.

The Great Spearwort (*Ranunculus ligua*), an ever more ▽ rare, robust herb of water-bank reeds, is one of the most poisonous species among the Buttercups.

Distribution of the Great Spearwort in Europe.

Siberia on the banks of lowland flowing and stagnant waters. Sometimes it is found in wet places which are flooded occasionally. It grows well in habitats which are warm and rich in nutrients in summer, but low in carbonates, in fine muddy humous soils. It was never abundant in Europe, but man's impact on water environments and marshy biotopes has turned in into a true rarity. It is protected by law in France and Germany. Fortunately, in Britain this plant is only rare in Scotland, but it and its habitats require protection nonetheless.

Of the monocotyledons, which in many ways resemble grasses, representatives of the Bur-reed (*Sparganium*) genus from the Bur-reed family (*Sparganiaceae*) grow next to the water. Conspicuous by virtue of its spiky achenes in fruits and orbicular flower heads, among the species which appeared on European red lists in the highest threat categories is the **Least Bur-reed** (*Sparganium minimum* Wallr.).

The Least Bur-reed is a perennial herb with a herbaceous stem which is either erect or floating on the water surface, simple and unbranched. The stem is about 0.75 m long. The leaves are very fine, grassy, flat and about 0.5 cm wide. The inflorescence on the end of the stem comprises 2—4 female and 1—2 male flower heads in the axil of the bracts. The flowers bloom from June to August.

It is a circumpolar plant widespread in northern Eurasia. In Europe it grows from lowland to medium mountain areas and it appears to be slightly oceanic. It is found in shallow mezotrophic (medium rich in nutrients) clean waters with a sandy or fine mud humous bottom. Apart from natural lakes, it also colonizes ditches and pools of peat-bogs, derelict gravel pits, etc. One way or another, it is a rare species. It is found in floating and submerged pads of water-lilies and pondweed.

In Britain the Least Bur-reed is more frequent in Scotland than in England, and it is unknown in Ireland. The pool community of which it is a characteristic member is now acutely endangered by modern land use. It was formerly more widespread in England, although it was probably inadequately recorded, but it is now in the endangered category.

A damp or wet site is required by plants from the ranks of the so-called messengers of spring — the Snowflake (*Leucojum*). It also belongs to the most well-known European protected species. In the plant system it belongs to the Daffodil family (*Amaryllidaceae*). The genera and species of this family have underground bulbs, linear leaves and conspicuous, regular flowers composed in a figure three (the

◁ The Least Bur-reed (*Sparganium minimum*) has an inflorescence with a small number of individual flower clusters, all of which grow at the base of the leaf-like bracts.

▽ The Summer Snowflake (*Leucojum aestivum*), a robust herb of flooded meadows and riverine woodland, has 3 to 7 flowers which grow on long thin stalks from a scape.

The Spring Snowflake (*Leucojum vernum*) often ▷ flowers before all the snow thaws. Sites in broadleaf woods have a greater chance of survival than those in farmed meadows.

The Taller Violet (*Viola elatior*) is notable for its ▷ large (up to 7 cm long) green, ovate lanceolate leaves ▽ with a stalk which is shorter than the stipules.

perianth is made up of two 3-part rings of petal-like segments). They are popular garden flowers cultivated in garden cultures. This also applies to both the European species of the snowflake described here.

Less known is the **Summer Snowflake** (*Leucojum aestivum* L.) which is generally more rare and also not so often cultivated in gardens. It is a perennial with an ovate bulb (about 3 cm in diameter), which grows to about 60 cm. One plant bears 3 to 7 white flowers, which are 1.5 to 2 cm long, growing on long, slender stalks from a spathe bract. It blooms in the middle of spring from April to May. The fruit capsules are round.

The Summer Snowflake is an inhabitant of wet, temporarily flooded woods and meadows near water courses. It requires clay and nutrient rich, medium humous soil. In central Europe it is a thermophile plant. It exists in southern and south-eastern Europe and to a lesser extent in central Europe, for example in the Danube basin and along its tributaries. Its occurrence in Germany is probably not native, but introduced or naturalized. It is protected by law in the Netherlands, France, Switzerland, Austria and the Czech and Slovak Republics.

The scattered colonies of Summer Snowflake in southern England as far north as Oxford and in western Ireland are believed to be native. Past losses of this plant are due not only to the destruction of their habitat, but also to uprooting. Fortunately the remaining populations are large and protected by their relative inaccessibility. Nevertheless the species is included in the British Red Data Book.

In the Czech Republic a large event took place several years ago devoted to the conservation of the Summer Snowflake. Virtually the only locations where this rare species could be found in south Moravia were to be flooded as a result of the construc-

tion of valley dams on the lower stretch of the Dyje River. In the course of a few years, conservation volunteers, raised from the future dam bed hundreds of thousands of specimens of Summer Snowflake and successfully replanted them in a suitable site in a nearby nature reserve.

The **Spring Snowflake** (*Leucojum vernum* L.) is shorter (10 to 30 cm high) with smaller bulbs (up to 2 cm in diameter) and with one, at most two flowers on the stem in the axil of a bract at the end of a scape. The flowers are 1.5 to 2.5 cm long and bloom — depending on their habitat — from March to April, often before the snow has melted. Two-flower scapes (and yellow stains under the tips of the perianth segments) are found on the more robust eastern subspecies, the **Carpathian Spring Snowflake** (*Leu-*

Distribution of the Spring Snowflake in Europe.

cojum vernum L. ssp. carpaticum (Spring) O. Schwarz), which grows in the Carpathian region.

Woodlands alongside lowland water courses are just one of the habitats of the Spring Snowflake. It also appears in large numbers in wet meadows and gorge forests in highlands as well as in mountain beech woods.

The Spring Snowflake is a central European species, protected in most countries and included in various threat categories. It is a very popular garden flower. The flowers are still sold at spring markets. The occurrence of the Spring Snowflake in gardens in some areas indicates that it grows wild there in the open countryside. However elsewhere it is often the case that today's population in the open countryside has been introduced by artificial methods. For example, any occurrences north of the Hannover-Wittenberg-Cottbus line in Germany are not considered to be indigenous. The plant is poisonous due to its content of the alkaloid leucine.

It appears that excessive picking and uprooting of the bulbs in some places really did weaken the Spring Snowflake population, but it is not certain if this caused its total extinction in certain areas. The plant faces a greater threat from modern farming methods. The greatest hope of survival for the Spring Snowflake is in forests, particularly in protected territories. The situation is worse in wet meadows which are 'recultivated' in various ways. For example, in Bohemia hundreds of thousands of bulbs were destroyed in this way, and only a few were transferred by conservationists to substitute habitats.

So if you chance to be in a forest in the early spring which is white with thousands of snowflake flowers, enjoy the view, as it is an increasingly rare one.

In Britain most occurrences of the Spring Snowflake (which is widely cultivated) are naturalized. Botanists, however, believe that two sites of occurrence in Somerset and Dorset, where it grows in damp scrub and on stream banks, can probably be regarded as native. It is included in the British Red Data Book.

In woods near lowland water courses another spring flower often associated with the snowflake is the **Alpine Squill** (*Scilla bifolia* L.) of the related Lily family (*Liliaceae*). This is a small perennial herb, 10 to 20 cm high. Most often one herbaceous stem with two broad linear ground leaves grows from a relatively large ovate to round bulb (up to 3 cm in diameter). There are 2—7 flowers in a raceme, sometimes more, and its supporting bracts are either stunted or missing completely. The corollas measure up to 12 cm in diameter and are bright pale blue, or

squills which are popular for their short growth and early spring flowers, particularly for rock gardens.

In Britain the Alpine Squill is not native, but it is sometimes found naturalized in gardens. The same applies to the **Siberian Squill** (*Scilla sibirica* Haw. in Andrews) from western Asia which, like the western Asian *Scilla amoena,* is cultivated throughout Europe and thrives in some areas as a result of naturalization.

Native British squills are the **Spring Squill** (*Scilla verna* Hudson), which flowers from April to June, and the **Autumn Squill** (*Scilla autumnalis* L.), which has small pinkish-blue flowers appearing from August to October. Neither is at all common and both grow on rocky and grassy places.

In Britain, particularly in England, bluebell woods are a characteristic spring feature. The **Bluebell**

sometimes pink or white. They bloom from the end of February to April depending on the habitat. In the early spring some areas are blue with squill but they soon disappear without a trace. The fruit — round capsules — contain seeds with a long, light appendage and they are spread by ants. Recently botanists divided the so-called large species — *Scilla bifolia* — into several smaller, very similar species.

The centre of the geographical range of the Alpine Squill is southern, particularly south-eastern Europe. From here it penetrates into central Europe, where it is relatively rare. It is often found in large populations, in woods and meadows alongside lowland water courses, but also in mixed broad-leaf groves of highlands, on wet, deep humous, nutrient-rich soil. It prefers calcareous soils.

The Alpine Squill is an ornamental flower and hence it attracts the attention of gardeners who sometimes uproot it in the wild to plant it in gardens. In the garden culture there are also several other

42

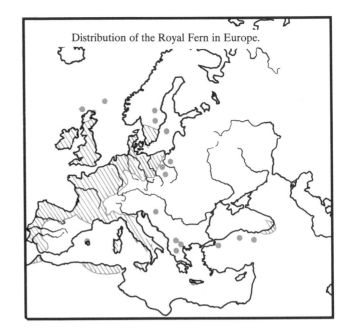

Distribution of the Royal Fern in Europe.

◁ ◁ The Floating Water-plantain (*Luronium natans*) is an inconspicuous herb growing on water banks. It has two types of leaves: basal submerged ones which are linear, and upper floating ones which are oval.

◁ Spring in a small broadleaved woodland in south-eastern England (end of April): hundreds and thousands of Bluebells (*Hyacinthoides nonscripta*) in the herb undergrowth.

◁ The Royal Fern (*Osmunda regalis*), a truly majestic
▽ feature of mainly woodland marshes, is conspicuous for its large segments of twice pinnated leaves.

The Ostrich-feather Fern (*Matteuccia struthiopteris*) ▷
produces brownish fruiting fronds in the centre of the ▽
tuft of fresh green leaves.

(*Hyacinthoides nonscripta* Houard ex Rothm.) is a very close relative of squills, and until recently was included in the squill genus. The flowers of the Bluebell are narrow, bell-shaped and violet-blue in colour, sometimes pinkish or white. Each flower has a pair of bracts at the base of the flower stalk. The 3 to 6 leaves are linear to linear lanceolate, and tip hooded. It grows in woods on lighter soils where it forms a blue carpet in early spring.

Britain's bluebell woods are now under threat from illegal harvesters. In some areas, particularly East Anglia, illegal harvesting is so intensive that it is possible that some bluebell woods will be destroyed completely. It is illegal to dig up wild bulbs without the landowner's permission, but the trade in wild-flower bulbs is considerable and growing. The British charity, Plantlife, struggling against this damage, estimated in 1993 that the trade from illegal harvesting is worth £1 million a year. Protected areas are an effective guarantee of bluebell preservation.

The woodland marshes in central European lowlands also have their rare species of violet — the European/western Siberian **Taller Violet** (*Viola elatior* Fries) of the Violet family (*Violaceae*). It is an easily recognizable species from a genus whose other members are sometimes difficult to identify. This perennial, relatively robust (20–50 cm high) herb has large (over 2 cm in diameter) light violet-blue flowers blooming from the end of spring (May) to the middle of summer (July). It is rare and on the decline, so it is usually found on central European red lists in the higher threat categories. Hence the occurrence of the Taller Violet is taken into account in the creation of a representative network of protected areas. This species is not native in Britain, it grows in the wild in France and is naturalized in Belgium.

The British Red Data Book includes an English fen species, which grows in Ireland in damp grassy hollows on limestone — the **Fen Violet** (*Viola persicifolia* Schreb.). It is a short, hairless perennial without a basal leaf-rosette, and has an erect stem with bluish-white flowers with violet veins. Flower-

ing in May and June, it grows in marshes, fens and fresh peat cuttings. Owing to the destruction of its habitats as a result of drainage, it has disappeared from some 20 known locations in England, remaining in one locality in Cambridgeshire. Numerous specimens of this protected plant reappeared in 1982 in a managed plot on a nature reserve in Cambridgeshire. There are scattered areas of occurrence in Ireland, where the plant does not seem to have declined so rapidly.

There are two more 'red' violets in Britain. **Tees-** **dale Violet** (*Viola rupestris* Schmidt), a short tufted plant with more rounded leaves and pale reddish-violet or whitish flowers (March to July) which grows in open, dry habitats on limestone. It is currently known to exist in 11 places in Yorkshire, Durham and Cumbria. **Dwarf Pansy** (*Viola kitaibeliana* Schmt.) is an annual with creamy flowers (March to July), similar to the common Field Pansy. It grows on the coast, in dunes and cliffs, on the Isles of Scilly and the Channel Islands.

The inconspicuous **Floating Water-plantain** (*Lur-*

onium natans (L.) Raf.) of the Water-plantain family (*Alismataceae*) grows by stagnant waters. It is one of the rarest European plants included in the European red list. It is a perennial herb with a leafy, 10 to 40 cm long creeping or floating stem. The submerged leaves are linear, the leaves floating on the surface are elongated to about 5 cm in length. In the axil of the leaves sometimes single and at other times 3—5 3-part white flowers bloom from May to September.

The Floating Water-plantain is a pioneer species of the flat shores of still waters and deeper swamps. It is fairly tolerant of short periods of drought. It is a sub-Atlantic plant which occurs mainly in areas of western Europe with an oceanic climate. It is one of many water and coastal species which are especially attractive and which would certainly disappear from the European flora without expert care.

The Floating Water-plantain is also mentioned in the British Red Data Book. The main areas where it occurs in Britain are northern Wales and Shropshire. It is intolerant of waters rich in phosphate and nitrate, where it is perhaps suppressed by more vigorous plants. The decline of the species is due to drainage and agricultural improvement. It is increasing, however, in canals: it has been introduced to several canal sites in Norfolk.

One of the most decorative of European ferns edging the banks of streams, often in large colonies, is the **Ostrich-feather Fern** (*Matteuccia struthiopteris* (L.) Todaro) of the Polypody family (*Polypodiaceae*). A funnel of bright green simple pinnate leaves, from 30 cm to 0.5 m long, issue from a scaly, long rhizome (over 0.5 m). Later so-called sporophyles — shorter fertile leaves — grow from the middle of the 'funnel'. They soon turn brown and carry spore-cases on their lobes.

The Ostrich-feather Fern is a Eurasian species. Central Europe is the western border of its range. Many botanists today believe that this border was moved artificially and that no original site exists in Germany nor in the Czech Republic. For a long time the Ostrich-feather Fern has been cultivated as a decorative plant in gardens, parks and in cemeteries. It grows easily in the wild on the banks of water courses, particularly streams and smaller rivers, from lowland to foothills. It can also be found in the undergrowth of alder woodlands. It is mainly endangered due to the canalization of these water courses and land use changes in its vicinity.

All the locations of Ostrich-feather Fern scattered over Britain are naturalized. In horticulture it is seen quite frequently.

Boggy habitats are also the home of other remarkable ferns. **Royal Fern** (*Osmunda regalis* L.) of the ancient Royal Fern family (*Osmundaceae*) sometimes grows to two metres in height. This perennial fern annually issues several long-stalked, elongated, double pinnate leaves in ovate segments from its branched ground rhizome. Either the entire leaf or parts of it are divided into the fertile and infertile organs. The rusty brown spore-cases are usually situated on the upper linear, wrinkled segmented leaves forming a more or less compact panicle.

The Royal Fern is also sometimes planted for decoration and so secondary habitats appear. As with some other fern, the dried ground rhizome of the Royal Fern is used as a substratum for the cultivation of house and glass-house epiphytic ornamental plants. It is also sometimes sold in this form in specialized shops.

It is a rare species, although widespread in its range. In Europe it has a clearly oceanic trend. It grows in peat-bogs, alder woodlands, on wet meadows, in forest ditches and marshes. It is especially abundant on the North Sea and Baltic coasts with occurrence declining inland. We know of only a few obviously native areas. The Royal Fern is protected by law in Germany, Poland, the Netherlands, Luxembourg, Austria and Switzerland. In the Czech Republic, where its only known location was in northern Bohemia, it was exterminated by habitat destruction. It penetrates southern central Europe from the Mediterranean area. However, there can be surprise occurrences of these rare and conspicuous plants. For example, several years ago participants in a young nature conservationists camp in south-western Hungary found the Royal Fern. It was the first finding in that country.

In Britain the Royal Fern can be found most frequently in coastal regions in the western parts of England, Scotland, Wales and Ireland. In some places it has been naturalized. Generally, and in inland England in particular, it can be regarded as a decreasing endangered species threatened by habitat loss and over-enthusiastic gardeners.

SPRINGS,
WET MEADOWS, FENS

The floristic wealth of European wet meadows (in the picture the Siberian Iris, *Iris sibirica*) is rapidly declining as a result of soil reclamation.

Meadows in alluvial valleys and on slopes with seepages belonged to the traditional European landscape. They were cut manually or by light mowers and the dried hay sometimes had to be left in the local hay lofts until winter, when the wet ground was frozen and the hay could be transported away.

Today every farmer uses heavy agricultural machinery, but a tractor cannot be used on these wet meadows because it would get bogged down in the wet, swampy ground. So the wet meadows are 'recultivated' — a system of drains is used to dry out the soil. After drainage, the ground is sowed with mixtures of grass — cultural fodder crops — or is converted into arable fields. Hardly anybody uses a scythe and rake to cut grass, and so smaller and less accessible wet meadows are not cultivated. Flying seeds settle in the meadows to give root to saplings and in a few decades the meadow turns into a clump of alders or ashes.

The semi-cultivated wet meadows do not provide any yield from the agricultural point of view. The growths of various sedges (*Carex*) and other hygrophilous herbs which predominate do not provide good quality fodder or hay. However, hundreds of interesting plant species are found in these communities. The drainage and conversion of meadows into forests reduces the wealth of these species and many disappear. Sometimes it is enough just to canalize the river or stream flowing through the meadows. In a deepened and walled bed water flows more quickly and does not have time to sink into the surroundings, the surface of ground water decreases and the meadows dry out.

The wet grasslands are some of the most endangered biotopes in Europe. Thousands of hectares disappear every day through the change of land use within an 'intensive' agriculture. Up until recently it was believed that many plant species of wet meadows only had a hope of survival in protected areas. However, it has been shown that maintaining a reserve in the state required — above all as far as the diverse and attractive species composition is concerned — requires a complex, scientifically based system of care. Perhaps this applies to wet meadows and seepages more than to any other endangered and protected biotope. These ecosystems were established, conditioned and preserved by human activities. The only way to ensure the preservation of a favourable environment in the reserves and protected areas is to copy or simulate the traditional land use of those habitats.

Just recently there has been a significant ray of hope of preserving the plant species of wet meadows, seepages and fens. It has been proved that these territories are not just habitats of remarkable and rare organisms and their entire communities, but that they also contribute towards the ecological stability of the countryside and therefore are of irreplaceable importance to the quality of our environment.

As we have already mentioned, grassy herbs of the Sedge (*Carex*) genus are found on wet grasslands in great abundance and diversity of species. Sedges are monocotyledonous herbs of the Sedge family (*Cyperaceae*), monoecious or dioecious plants, with flowers in spikelets carried on 3-angled stems. The pollinated female flowers ripen in closed achenes in dense bracts. This fruit is botanically known as a sack. The sedge's sacks are one of the most important features by which the various species of sedge can be distinguished. It is sometimes very difficult to distinguish these plants and often totally impossible for a layperson. People usually ignore or do not know what to do with the unattractive, inconspicuous

grassy looking herb. Despite this, various species of sedges are very important. Some are abundant, characteristic species of certain plant communities with precisely and narrowly defined habitat demands and, as such, they are important biological indicators of soil, the water regime, etc.

One of these species is **Davall Sedge** (*Carex davalliana* S.M.). It is a perennial, 20—40 cm high, thick tufted herb. The stems and leaves are coarse, the bristled and troughshaped leaves with brown tufted sheaths are always shorter than the stems. It has numerous stems with solitary, rather sparse cylindrical spikelets 1 to 2 cm long. The sacks, about 4 mm in length, slowly narrow down into thin beaks. The Davall Sedge is a spring species, flowering from April to June.

On suitable habitats the Davall Sedge forms entire thick lawns. It is the leading, characteristic species of the union of plant communities called *Caricion davallianae.* These are mossy communities of lowland fens and fen meadows as well as seepages at higher altitudes (up to 1,800 m above sea level) always found in mineral rich, calcareous wet ground. The Davall Sedge is an all-European species, most often found in central Europe. In the northern part of Europe it was never abundant; however, it was commonly found in many areas of Bavaria, Bohemia and Austria. In view of the disturbance of the biotopes of wet meadows due to human intervention, it has also become a rarity in these regions. It is on European red lists in various categories of endangerment. Together with this sedge and its community, numerous other species are also disappearing, sometimes conspicuous, ornamental and interesting as far as their economic use is concerned.

The Davall Sedge has been recorded in only three sites in Britain: two in Yorkshire and one in Somer-

set. The latter was a boggy area near Bath which was drained and built upon in about 1845. This species is now extinct in Britain.

The British Red Data Book includes 13 other species of sedges; at least half of them are wetland plants.

From among the rare and threatened rushes (*Juncus*), an example is the **Dark Rush** (*Juncus atratus* Krocker). This relatively robust, 25 cm to 1 m high perennial received its scientific species name from its glossy black-brown perianth segments. It flowers from July to August. Another important distinguishing feature of the species is the protruding longitudinal ribs of the rounded greyish green leaves.

This is a European/western Siberian species. It grows on lowland fen meadows which are rich in mineral matter, in flooded derelict gravel pits and

peat ditches or on the edge of waters and ditches. In central Europe Dark Rush is clearly on the decline. It is listed as a species in the highest threat category on the red list of Germany.

There are some twenty native rush species in the British flora; the Dark Rush is not among them. Six species are included in the British Red Data Book. **Thread Rush** (*Juncus filiformis* L.), a slender and wiry perennial up to 40 cm in height, grows on the stony margins of lakes and reservoirs in Leicestershire, Yorkshire, Durham, Cumberland, Fife, Stirlingshire and Kincardineshire. It is currently on the increase and is possibly spread by birds carrying its seed. **Dwarf Rush** (*Juncus capitatus* Weigel) is a dwarf (15—10 cm high) annual with flowers in terminal clusters which grows on damp heaths. It is now known to exist in 16 locations in Cornwall; it also occurs in the Channel Islands.

Another endangered and disappearing grass-like plant of wet habitats is the **German Asphodel** (*Tofieldia calyculata* (L.) Wahlenb.), belonging to the refined Lily family (*Liliaceae*). It is a perennial, 10—30 cm high herb. Its erect leafy stems with linear, lanceolate, multiveined, 2—4 mm wide leaves grow from a short rhizome. The stems are terminated in a cylindrical raceme (2—10 cm long) of small yellowish white flowers which bloom at the beginning of the summer — from June to July.

The German Asphodel grows from foothills to the alpine level (at an altitude over 2,000 m above sea level) in the Pyrenees, the Alps and Carpathian mountains. It can sometimes be found in central European lowlands — in the northern part of Germany and in central Bohemia in the Elbe basin. Its habitats are wet meadows, damp, constantly washed down rocks and seepages. It grows almost exclusively in calcareous soils which are rich in minerals.

In lowlands, the biotopes of the German Asphodel are under great pressure from civilization, and hence this herb is greatly endangered there. It is listed in the highest threat category on the German and Czech red lists. The only hope of preservation for this plant lies in well-managed reserves in lowland areas, although there is no danger yet that the German Asphodel will become extinct on higher ground in the Alps and Carpathians, especially where national parks and other protected areas have been set up.

As an Arctic-alpine relict from the ice age, the **Scottish Asphodel** (*Tofieldia pusilla* (Michx) Pers) can only be found on high mountains in meadows near springs and on wet rocks.

This is, in contrast to the German species, a plant which is native in Britain. It is a shorter plant than the German Asphodel, but very similar to it, with small white or greenish flowers (June — August). The rather rare Scottish Asphodel occurs from Yorkshire northwards.

A beautiful feature of wet meadows, particularly if found in larger masses, are the wild **Gladioli** (*Gladiolus*) with ornamental flowers. In shape (not in size) they resemble cultivated garden gladioli. They belong to the Iris family (*Iridaceae*). In Europe gladioli growing wild have flowers only about 2 cm long in various shades of purplish-red colours. In the

Distribution of the Siberian Iris in Europe.

ground they have ovate bulbs, and their erect stems carry 2—3 sword-shaped leaves.

The **Swamp Gladiolus** (*Gladiolus palustris* Gaud.) grows to a height of 30—60 cm. The leaves are only 4—9 mm wide, the floral odd raceme is sparse with 2—5 flowers. The lower petals of this species tend to be whitish and spotted. It flowers from June (or even from May) to July.

The Swamp Gladiolus is a south European plant and grows in small groups on wet boggy meadows from lowland up to lower mountain areas (in the Alps). Due to land use changes, it has already become extinct in many European regions and is on the decline in all others.

The **Roof Gladiolus** (*Gladiolus imbricatus* L.) tends to be taller, up to about 0.75 m in height, has broader leaves (up to 2 cm) and a thicker odd raceme (with up to 10 flowers). It flowers a little later — in July and August. It is a somewhat more abundant species and grows mainly in eastern Europe. The western border of its range (apart from western Germany) passes across central Europe. It grows on wet meadows in large populations and is also a characteristic species of the *Molinion* union. People pick it for its ornamental appearance for use in bouquets. Formerly it used to occur secondarily as a weed in fields, for example among potatoes and oats in the Jeseníky Mountains in northern Moravia. Modern methods of farming are eliminating it from the open countryside.

Neither of these gladioli is cultivated in gardens. The bulbs contain interesting matter and some species of gladioli were formerly used as curative drugs. Both gladioli are beautiful ornaments of natural protected areas and have little hope of survival in Europe outside these territories.

Only a single species of Gladiolus is found in the wild in Britain: the west European and west Asian **Wild Gladiolus** (*Gladiolus illyricus* Koch). This medium sized perennial with 3—10 reddish-purple flowers, 2.5—4.5 cm long, the lower petals zoned with white and dark red, grows in open woodland, scrub and heaths, sometimes in slightly marshy habitats. It occurs only in Hampshire now, mainly in the New Forest. Although the plant is legally protected, it is regularly picked in large numbers. On the Isle of Wight it became extinct in 1897. Introductions of this species have been recorded from Devon and the Channel Islands.

◁ The Yellow-wort (*Blackstonia perfoliata*) has flowers with long calyx lobes in lax-branched clusters; if they are of the same length as the golden-yellow corolla then this is *Blackstonia perfoliata* subsp. *acuminata* which is sometimes considered to be a separate species. The picture was taken in the Danubian basin.

◁ The Marsh Gladiolus (*Gladiolus palustris*), with its
▽ lovely pinkish-violet flowers in a lax raceme, is on the verge of extinction as a result of the drainage, fertilization and transformation of meadows.

The Blue Iris (*Iris spuria*) can be recognized by its ▷ yellowish-violet flowers and broadly lanceolate linear ▽ leaves; it is a thermophilous species and can also tolerate a certain amount of salt in the soil.

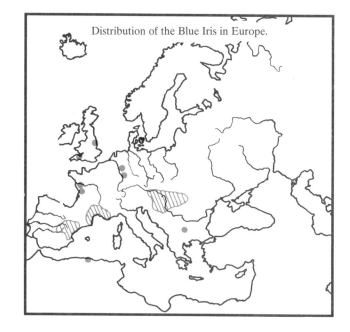

Distribution of the Blue Iris in Europe.

In the wet meadows of Europe one also finds the beautiful, rare and endangered species of the *Iris* genus whose name is carried by the Iris family (*Iridaceae*) of plants.

The **Siberian Iris** (*Iris sibirica* L.) is a perennial tufted herb over 1 metre in height. Erect, rounded, rather thin stems grow from a creeping rhizome. The leaves are narrow (up to 0.5 cm wide), sword-like, shorter than the inflorescence. The very decorative blue-violet, sometimes whitish flowers with a pleasant scent grow from the axil of bracts mainly in pairs. They bloom at the end of spring — from May to June.

The Siberian Iris is a Euro-Siberian plant. In central Europe it used to grow in abundance in wet meadows (characteristic species of the community of the blue moor-grass) or in shore reeds and in marshes in woods, from lowlands to lower mountains. Economic development with all its damaging consequences for these biotopes have eradicated it from many regions. However, fortunately the Siberian Iris can be transferred successfully from endangered places to suitable substitute habitats.

A rarer and more endangered species is the blue-violet flowering **Blue Iris** (*Iris spuria* L.). It is a shorter perennial (30—50 cm) with tough, narrow, swordlike leaves about 1 cm wide. There are 1—4 blue-violet flowers with yellow stripes and, as in the Siberian species, they bloom from the end of May to June.

The Blue Iris is a plant of lowland meadows growing from western Europe to the Balkans. To a certain extent, it is a thermophilous species and also withstands a certain amount of salt in the ground. In the Pannonian region and its borderlands (Hungary, southern Slovakia) it is also found in salt marshes. It is a great rarity in many European countries. In Britain it is very rare, confined to ditches in Dorset and in Lincolnshire. It may originally have been introduced into England.

Both of the above-mentioned species of irises are protected by law in the countries where they grow. In some countries, such as Austria, Switzerland and parts of Germany, the **Yellow Iris** (*Iris pseudacorus* L.) with its large yellow flowers is also protected. It is, however, still found in abundance on the edge of waters, forest pools, ditches and riverside woods throughout Britain.

The irises are plants with an ancient tradition in folk medicine and in the cosmetics and perfume industries. Their rhizomes contain remarkable and precious chemical substances. In this respect, of course, some south European species were formerly

cultivated throughout Europe for use as well as decoration. The marshy species, which we mentioned briefly, are sometimes used in horticulture — either directly as decorative botanical species or as plant material for cultivation.

The meadow marshes are also the habitats of some of the most rare and threatened European species of the Orchid family (*Orchidaceae*). In Europe wild orchids do not grow on the trunks or in the crowns of trees (epiphytically) as in the tropics, but root in the ground: they are terrestrial plants. With some exceptions, they do not have large flowers; nevertheless, on closer investigation their flowers, usually in a thick, spiky inflorescence, attractive in shape and colour, reveal their membership of the 'aristocratic' plant family.

Such a species is the **Marsh Helleborine** (*Epipactis palustris* (Mill.) Crantz). It is a perennial, 25 to 50 cm high. In the ground it has a long creeping protruding rhizome from which stems grow annually with several (on average about 5) leaves, elongated ovate at the bottom and lanceolate at the top. In the upper part the stems have short hairs and bear a one-sided inflorescence (up to 20 cm long) consisting of 8—30 flowers. The flowers are pendulous, and hang from the stem. They are quite big, up to 4 cm long, with hairy ovules. The lip has no spur and is divided into two parts: the back — so-called hypochil — is fleshy,

the front — so-called epichil — is flat and mobile when it is windy. The flowers are white with a varied pinkish violet tint and veins. They bloom from June to August.

The Marsh Helleborine is a Eurasian species and does not grow in some parts of southern Europe, but is found in central parts of North Africa. It is quite clearly a calcicolous plant, growing above all on the fens in the communities of the Davall Sedge and the Blue Moor-grass (*Caricion davallianae* and *Molinion*), occasionally also among reeds and sedge tussocks. On the North Sea coast, e.g. in the Netherlands, it grows on marshes in small valleys between sand dunes. It is scattered throughout central Europe and more concentrated on the edge of the Alps and the Carpathian region. It grows up to about 1,000 m above sea level.

In Britain it used to be common as far north as Perth, and was rare in Ireland, but it is now declining.

Agricultural improvements cause great damage to this plant. The cause is not only drainage, but also fertilization. The Marsh Helleborine is also seriously on the decline in places where wet meadows are not mowed and so turn into scrub and woodland. Like many wild orchids *Epipactis palustris* is considered to be threatened in most European countries in which it grows and is also protected by law in most parts of central Europe.

Britain has its own endemic species among the Helleborines. This is the **Dune Helleborine** (*Epipactis dunensis* (T.T.A. Stephenson) Godfrey), a small orchid with long pointed, recurved pale pink or greenish lips. It flowers on maritime sand-dunes in June and July, restricted to north Wales and north-western England. There are currently about a dozen locations where small populations exist.

▽ ◁ The Marsh Helleborine (*Epipactis palustris*), considered to be one of the loveliest of European terrestrial orchids of boggy, usually calcareous meadows, is becoming a rarity.

◁ The Lax-flowered Orchid (*Orchis laxiflora*) has only shallow lobes of a distinctly large bottom lip. The centre of its range is in south-eastern Europe; it also grows in salty soils.

The Marsh Gentian (*Gentiana pneumonanthe*), with ▷ its campanulate flowers at the base of the upper leaves, is ▽ an increasingly rare species of wet meadows found in lowlands right up to foothills. Its inability to compete with other species intensifies its vulnerability.

Distribution of the Marsh Gentian in Europe.

Some are protected in nature reserves. The species is included in the British Red Data Book.

The **Marsh Orchid** (*Orchis palustris* Jacq.) is a perennial with a ground orbicular tuber, 25—50 cm high when in flower. It differs from the other species of its family because its basal leaves do not come together at ground level into some sort of rosette, but are scattered round the stem. 3—4 leaves have flowers and they are very narrow (usually only about 1 cm wide), lanceolate to linear. The inflorescence is also very conspicuous. It is a relatively loose cylindrical spike. The individual flowers are up to 2.5 cm long, pink-violet, purple with whitish spots, and, less frequently, pure white. They have a large 3-lobed lip and a short, blunt and cylindrical spur. They flower in June and July.

The Marsh Orchid is a Mediterranean plant and rarely grows as far north as central Europe. As a consequence of various land improvement works it is an endangered species today and is very rare. The Marsh Orchid is found on calcareous, elsewhere also on slightly acidic meadows, above all on fens, and it also withstands a certain amount of salt in the soil. It is light-loving and thermophile, and is very sensitive to any changes in its site, especially the water regime. If the site is disturbed, then individual plants become stunted, their number decreases and then the species becomes extinct altogether.

The almost 1 m high, robust **Loose-flowered Orchid** (*Orchis laxiflora* Lam.) is larger and greater. It has wider leaves (about 3 cm) and undivided or only a 3-lobed lip in flower. The flowering plant protruding from the shallow water of flooded meadows provide a splendid view. It is also the sole European orchid which can be classified as a salinic species, famous for its occurrence on the salt marshes of the Hungarian puszta. Experts which is a south-east European plant and central Europe is only on the very edge of its range. Experts have not yet reached a conclusion about the taxonomic status of this species. Most often in recent times, the *Orchis palustris* is also classified as a subspecies: *Orchis laxiflora* ssp. *palustris* (Jacq.) Aschers. et Graebn. What is certain

is that *Orchis laxiflora palustris* is extinct in western Germany today and endangered in the Czech and Slovak Republics, Austria and Hungary. In Britain, the Loose-flowered Orchid is native only in Jersey and Guernsey, but — oddly enough — is not included in the British Red Data Book.

The **Marsh Gentian** (*Gentiana pneumonanthe* L.) of the Gentian family (*Gentianaceae*) requires special care in its remaining habitats. So far it has evaded waterworks, recultivation, farming and other damaging activities due to a decree of special protection. It is a perennial herb growing to a height of 20 to 40 cm, hairless without a ground leaf rosette (which is found, however, in some mountain gentians), with linear to linear lanceolate leaves, more or less one-

◁ The Bogbean (*Menyanthes trifoliata*) has large trifoliate leaves and, on a leafless scape, flowers in a dense raceme.

The Marsh Felwort (*Swertia perennis*) has five nar- ▷ row, steelish blue corolla lobes and five stamens: it ▽ grows in mountain flushes and wet rocks (the picture is from the Slovak Carpathians) and, more rarely, on lowland wet meadows.

The Common Butterwort (*Pinguicula vulgaris*), con- ▷ spicuous for its fleshy leaves, can withstand trampling and grazing, but is a weak competitor against other plant species.

veined growing on opposite sides of the stem. The 1—3 bell-like flowers on the end of the erect stems have rich dark blue corollas with five green stripes inside. They bloom from July to September or October, when the first frost burns them brown.

The Marsh Gentian is a European/west Siberian species scattered throughout Europe on grasslands which are not calcareous, from lowland areas through hill country right up to foothills. It used to be picked as a medicinal plant for its content of mustard in the rhizome and stalk. It probably never grew in abundance, but changes in land-use in recent decades have caused a critical decline in its population.

The protection of the Marsh Gentian was one of the determining factors for the declaration of some protected areas. However, the protection of territories alone is not enough for the plant. The Marsh Gentian is a characteristic species of the union of communities with the Blue Moor-grass (*Molinion*) and is suppressed by the stock-piling of dried old grass on meadows which are no longer mowed because they are protected. The removal of grass from the previous year, which now takes place in a number of central European reserves, achieves effective results. *Gentiana pneumonanthe* has survived and even thrived in these areas.

An interesting experience was noted in the English county of Shropshire. The Marsh Gentian appears there as an extremely rare plant in open trampled patches in damp heathland. The plant is clearly a poor competitor with taller plants unless these are grazed and trampled. The only remaining area of occurrence in Shropshire is protected by informal agreement, which is another way of protecting rare and endangered species. In Britain generally, Marsh Gentian is scattered throughout Sussex, Cumbria and Anglesey.

A very important and very useful plant, from the human point of view, is a species of wet habitats belonging to the Gentian family *(Gentianaceae)*, called the **Bogbean** (*Menyanthes trifoliata* L.). Some experts place it in the special Bogbean family *(Menyanthaceae)*. As the German common name 'marsh clover' or the older English name 'marsh trefoil' indicate, the most conspicuous feature of this perennial is the trifoliate leaves resembling the large leaves of the clover. The entire plant usually grows to a height of 20—30 cm. The highly ornamental flowers, crowded into an erect thick raceme, are white or pinkish, with a broad campanulate corolla, deeply divided into fringed lobes. It blooms from the end of spring — in May and June. The Bogbean is a medicinal and aromatic plant which is utilized in the pharmaceutical and food industry. When in flower, it is picked for its leaves which contain mustard. It provides a drug which encourages the activity of glands, the excretion of stomach juices, creation of blood and strengthening of the entire organism. The effective substances are also found in abundance in the thick, creeping, segmented rhizome which, however, is no longer picked today because the plant is protected in several European countries.

The Bogbean is a circumpolar species, widespread in the northern part of the Earth's temperate zone. It is found in various types of marshes: from alkaline fens rich in minerals, to acid peat-bogs, on wet meadows, on the banks of stagnant waters, in shore sedge tussocks, in pools and ditches. It is a significant infill plant in the vegetation of shallow waters. This plant used to be widespread throughout Europe from the lowlands right up to the mountains (in the Alps up to about 1,800 m above sea level) although it never grew in abundance. However, as a consequence of various interventions and changes in the cultivation of marsh biotopes, it is on the decline and has become a rarity in many regions.

Fortunately, it is still common throughout Britain, and sometimes even grows in abundance in localized areas.

Several specialized institutions have shown an interest in the Bogbean in recent years as a medicinal and aromatic plant. For example in the Czech Republic there has been research into the possibility of introducing this plant to some sort of natural semiculture, mainly into artificial water reservoirs where it could be harvested regularly. The landscape would also benefit from this process as it is an ornamental plant.

Another rare and threatened plant which requires protection and belongs to the Gentian family is the **Yellow-wort** (*Blackstonia perfoliata* L. Huds.). It is a hairless, grey coloured annual of about 30 cm in height. The simple stems with opposite triangular ovate leaves are only sparsely branched on the upper part. The 6- to 8-part flowers have golden-yellow corollas. They bloom throughout the summer from June to September.

The Yellow-wort is basically a Mediterranean species and the northern border of its geographical range crosses western and central Europe. It grows on damp and wet meadows in various soils, poor in humus but calcareous. It also penetrates into medium fresh grasslands with Brome (*Bromus*) and Blue Moor-grass (*Molinia*).

In Britain, the Yellow-wort is scattered throughout England, as well as in Jersey and southern Ireland. Formerly it was used as a medicinal plant.

A remarkable plant of the wet biotopes in Europe from lowlands to high mountains is the **Marsh Felwort** (*Swertia perennis* L.), which is also a member of the Gentian family.

The Marsh Felwort is a perennial herb growing to a height of up to about 0.5 m. It has erect, angular stems branched only at the ends of the inflorescence. The basal leaves form a rosette. The flowers in a racemose inflorescence are relatively small (up to

2.5 cm in diameter), a violet-blue or steel greyish-blue with darker spots, 5-part and greenish at the mouth of the corolla. They bloom from June to September.

The Marsh Felwort is a circumpolar species with a certain Arctic-Alpine trend, not native in Britain. In central Europe it is found in the north German lowland on the fens. Otherwise it grows on mountain wet meadows and seepages up to 2,500 m above sea level. The smaller subspecies *Swertia perennis* L. ssp. *alpestris* (Baumg.) Simonka is found at altitudes above 1,500 m. The Marsh Felwort grows in German and Czech mountains including the Bavarian Forest, the Bohemian Forest, the Ore Mountains, the Sudeten Mountains, the Alps and the higher areas of the Carpathians. In Slovakia it is often found in deep rocky limestone canyons, on wet rocks (Malá Fatra, Slovenský Raj). The drainage and intensive cultivation of the wet meadows is destroying its habitats in the lowlands and foothills. The Marsh Felwort is protected by law in Germany and Switzerland.

The water and marsh biotopes are the habitats of interesting, carnivorous plants, which supplement their diet by trapping small animals, especially insects. One of them is the **Common Butterwort** (*Pinguicula vulgaris* L.) of the Butterwort family (*Lentibulariaceae*). This perennial herb has fleshy, elongated ovate leaves, curved upwards at the edges. The leaves are 3–10 cm long and there are up to 10 of them forming a leaf-rosette which grows close to the ground. At a height of up to 15 cm, 1–2 cm long flowers with a blue-violet bilabiate spurred corolla grow – only one on each stalk. It blooms from May to July.

The thick leaves are the organs with which the plant traps the tiny insects. There are sticky glands on the surface of the leaves to which the insects stick and the plant digests them. The sticky secretion of the

glands contains digestive enzymes and also pinguiculatryptaz ferment which curdles milk (the plant was used for this purpose in several European mountainous regions and northern countries).

Not much chemical and pharmacological research has been undertaken into the content of the substances of the Common Butterwort which have curative properties. In some countries this species is on the official lists of medicinal plants. The drug from its stalk (*Herba pinguiculae*) reduces cramp, increases the secretion of the upper respiratory tracts and also has insecticidal effects. It is used for coughs particularly in children, and was once a favoured drug for all lung diseases.

The Common Butterwort is a circumpolar northern species. It is spread across Europe from lowland fens to rocky seepages in the mountains up to an altitude of about 1,500 m above sea level, but it is also found in acid peat-bogs which are low in nutrients. Many of its habitats, particularly in the lowlands, hilly country and foothills are disappearing due to the destruction of the biotopes.

The **Large-flowered Butterwort** (*Pinguicula grandiflora* Lam.), a west European species with large deep-violet flowers, grows on acid bogs and wet rocks and flushes. In Britain it is confined to southwestern Ireland, and has been naturalized in Cornwall. A smaller species with yellow or pale coloured flowers and greyish leaves is the **Pale Butterwort** (*Pinguicula lusitanica* L.). This is also a west European species, scattered throughout Britain where it occurs on the Isle of Wight, in the Outer Hebrides, on Orkney Islands and in most of Ireland.

The **Alpine Butterwort** (*Pinguicula alpina* L.) is a high mountain species. It has yellowish white flowers, with two yellow spots on the bottom lip. This Alpine-Arctic species (widespread in Europe in the main mountainous areas and in the north) grows in wet, particularly rocky habitats, above all limestone and dolomitic rocks up to almost 2,500 m above sea level. Under suitable conditions, for example in the deep rocky canyons of the Slovak Carpathians, it is found at lower altitudes.

In the British Red Data Book the Alpine Butterwort is marked as extinct. It was only known to exist in one British location in Easter Ross, where it was first reported in 1831, and apparently destroyed around 1900 because of the growth of pines. In most European states the Butterworts are protected by law.

An interesting plant is the **Fritillary** (*Fritillaria*) of the Lily family (*Liliaceae*). In the open countryside of central and western Europe one rarely finds the **Snakeshead Fritillary,** also called **Snakeshead Lily** (*Fritillaria meleagris* L.). It grows on damp to wet meadows that are cultivated by traditional methods. Formerly it was obviously more widespread, and some botanists even claim that a certain method of cultivation of meadows by man led to its increase in the not too distant past. However, today the Snakeshead Fritillary is disappearing as a result of changes in the cultivation of these habitats.

It is a perennial with a globular ground bulb about 1 cm in diameter. Every year a 15 to 30 cm high herbaceous stem with 4 to 5 linear, grey-green leaves grows from the bulb. The erect stem droops slightly at the end and carries 1 or 2 nodding campanulate flowers measuring about 3 cm in diameter. The flowers are purple brown and chequered. The Snakeshead Fritillary is a spring flower; it blooms in April and May, sometimes even earlier.

The centre of the geographical range of the Snakeshead Fritillary is western European with a certain sub-Atlantic tendency. This very rare, en-

dangered, decorative, but poisonous species is protected by law almost all over Europe.

The German international foundation Stiftung Natur und Pflanzen (Nature and Plants Foundation) chose the Snakeshead Fritillary as the 'Flower of the Year 1993' as a symbol of the European plants in danger. Also in Britain the species is in the sights of nature-lovers and conservationists. In the first edition of the British Vascular Plants Red Data Book (1977) it was included as vulnerable. The fact that it was omitted from the second edition (1983) does not rule out the threats: picking and grazing during the flowering season prevent regeneration by seed, and the drainage, ploughing and artificial fertilization of

its habitats have caused a dramatic decline in populations which once numbered thousands of plants on one single site. The protected Snakeshead Fritillary is native in southern and central England; elsewhere it has been introduced artificially.

In our selection from the wet biotopes, we have already mentioned some species which are found in high mountains and rarely in lower lying areas, above all in the Alpenvorland (northern foothills of the Alps) and in the Quaternary lowlands of northern central Europe. One of the species of this type is the lovely representative of the Primrose family (*Primulaceae*) — the **Birdseye Primrose** (*Primula farinosa* L.). The scientific name of this 5 to 20 cm high perennial is derived from the white mealy substance on the undersides of the leaves and on the scape and stalks and calyxes. A rosette of ground leaves grows from an underground rhizome and from the rosette on a scape grows a thick umbel of pinkish-violet flowers which measures 1 — 1.5 cm in diameter. The flowers bloom at the end of spring — from May to June and later in high mountain areas.

The Birdseye Primrose is an Arctic-Alpine species. It is very rarely found on the fens in the northern parts of Germany and Poland. As a consequence of changes to entire biotopes, it is on the decline and is an endangered species. It fares better on wet, regularly mowed meadows in the Bavarian Alpenvorland. Its best prospects of survival lie in the most abundant European occurrences on damp meadows and seepages in the mountains where the plant grows to an altitude of almost 2,500 m above see level. In the mountain environment, especially in the Alps, a layperson can easily confuse it with a number of rather similar species of primrose.

It is a conspicuous, ornamental spring flower and a favourite for cultivation with rock gardeners. The

rhizome contains saponin. In central Europe it is one of the species protected by law. Its occurrence in lower areas has motivated the establishment of protected territories. The complex problems of the most suitable form of management are now being resolved within these territories so that the population does not decline in number or vitality. In Britain, the Birdseye Primrose is confined to northern England, where it grows locally.

A plant very similar to it — broader leaves and broader lobes of the dark purple corolla distinguish it — is the **Scottish Primrose** (*Primula scotica* Hooker). It is an endemic of Scotland, where it grows in maritime turf in Sutherland, Caithness and Orkney with a single isolated location in Easter Ross. Because of the relatively high number of areas of occurrence it is not believed to be endangered, although it is threatened by oil industry developments and mentioned in the British Red Data Book.

In times gone by, when summer ended and students returned to their desks, an attractive white flower used to bloom in abundance on wet meadows and, because of the time when it bloomed (August to September), it earned the German folk name of the 'student rose'. The **Grass-of-Parnassus** (*Parnassia palustris* L.) is in fact related to the Rose family, although it is now classified by botanists in a separate Grass-of-Parnassus family (*Parnassiaceae*). This perennial herb, with a slanting thick rhizome and a ground leaf-rosette, has a 5—25 cm high erect stem ending with one solitary 5-part flower (2—3 cm in diameter) with pure white or pale pink petals.

The Grass-of-Parnassus is a circumpolar species widespread in the northern part of the Earth's temperate zone. It grows on fens and wet meadows from lowlands to mountains (over 2,000 m above sea level). It is interesting that in the mountains it flowers earlier than in the lowlands (in June and July). It is also found there in very short forms on wet rocks and damp scree. It mainly inhabits calcareous ground and is a biological indicator of wet habitats. However, times have changed since it used to bloom in abundance. Fens and wet meadows have declined and the formerly quite common Grass-of-Parnassus is now appearing on European red lists in various threat categories. It is protected by law in Belgium and the Netherlands where it grows mainly near the North Sea coast on the marshes in depressions between the higher sand dunes. Also in Britain the

⊲ The Yellow Marsh Saxifrage (*Saxifraga hirculus*) with
▽ its yellow flowers, is a bog plant, contrary to its generic name.

The Adder's Tongue (*Ophioglossum vulgatum*) is an in- ▷ conspicuous plant usually concealed in wet meadow grass, with a leaf-like frond divided into an ovate assimilating part and a linear fruiting spike.

The Moor-king (*Pedicularis sceptrum-carolinum*) ▷ ▷ has a raceme of flowers which truly resembles a royal sceptre: the red margins of the lower lips look like rubies.

Grass-of-Parnassus used to be widespread, and is now decreasing. Some English botanists considered it 'one of the most curious and beautiful of our native plants', and as far back as half a century ago they expressed the fear that 'it may be slowly dying out'.

Similar to the Grass-of-Parnassus family is the Saxifrage family (*Saxifragaceae*) which mainly embraces species found in rocky and scree habitats. Nevertheless, there is one species in European flora whose typical habitat is meadow marshes and that is the **Yellow Marsh Saxifrage** (*Saxifraga hirculus* L.). It is a rare, endangered plant in need of protection.

The Yellow Marsh Saxifrage is a thin, perennial herb growing to 10—30 cm in height. This species does not have the typical ground-leaf rosette like other Saxifrages. The ascendant two erect stems are rich in leaves, most of which grow in its upper part, but sparse in terms of flowers. The 1—3 flowers are quite large (1.5 — 2 cm in diameter), 5-part with bright yellow and sometimes reddish spotted petals. They bloom from July to August.

In west and central European flora this circumpolar, northern to Arctic plant features rarely. It grows on wet meadows and peat-bogs in lowlands and foothills. It has survived in Poland only at the foot of the Carpathians and in the German Alpenvorland.

In Britain, the Yellow Marsh Saxifrage is rare, with about 20 areas of occurrence in northern England, middle and southern Scotland and Ireland. Many of the locations recorded previously do not exist any more. The species has declined abruptly because of drainage and the improvement of upland pastures. It is a British Red Data Book plant, four of its occurrences are currently protected by National Nature Reserves.

Several species of the interesting Meadow-rue (*Thalictrum*) of the Buttercup family (*Ranunculaceae*) are found on European marsh meadows. As opposed to many other Buttercup family species, the plants of this genus do not have the conspicuous large flowers, but very small yellowish flowers grouped into rich panicles. These are perennial herbs, from 0.5 to over 1 m in height with pinnate leaves. They bloom in the summer months.

The **Shining Meadow Rue** (*Thalictrum lucidum* L.) with pleasantly scented flowers, grows to a height of 60—120 cm. The western border of its range reaches central Europe, running roughly from the Baltic (Mecklenburg) south to Bavaria, so it does not occur in Britain. It is sometimes found on wet meadows with the Meadowsweet (*Filipendula ulmaris*), the Marsh Marigold (*Caltha palustris*) and the Molinia. One can also find it in thickets and woods at the water's edge.

Similar is the **Common Meadow Rue** (*Thalictrum flavum* L.), a Euro-Siberian species of riverside meadows, native in Britain. This tallest of all British meadow rues grows in wet, grassy habitats as far north as Inverness, including Ireland. It is confined to lowland, was never common and is steadily decreasing now due to human impact on wetlands.

Even a careful observer can sometimes miss the inconspicuous but remarkable fern of the Adder's Tongue family (*Ophioglossaceae*) — **Adder's Tongue** (*Ophioglossum vulgatum* L.) — among tall grasses. It is a perennial fern rarely higher than 10 cm. Annually one, or very rarely two leaves appear from a ground rhizome. It looks as if a spike with spore-cases grew from the axil of the leaf. In fact these are two sections of one leaf: the infertile, yellowish green elongated ovate section and the fertile, linear-lanceolate, long-stalked section with spore-cases on both sides of the central nerve.

This fern is circumpolar and grows in Europe on wet and damp meadows, above all as a characteristic species in the union of the plant communities of the blue moor-grass, in base rich, frequently calcareous soils. In the mountains it grows up to 1,000 m above sea level. With the decline of suitable biotopes, its areas of occurrence are also declining and hence it appears in various threat categories on European red lists.

The Adder's Tongue is fairly evenly distributed over Britain, more common in some regions of England, apparently more rare in Scotland. It is tolerant of heavy grazing, but a poor competitor in tall, dense vegetation. It is decreasing, but may be much more common than believed because it is so difficult to find.

The British Red Data Book includes the Mediterranean **Lusitanian Adder's Tongue** (*Ophioglossum lusitanicum* L.) formerly believed to be only a variety of the Adder's Tongue from which it differs in its small size (about 5 cm). It is usually found only in water near the sea in the Isles of Scilly and on Guernsey.

We have left until last the king of European marsh biotopes. **Moor-king** is the English name of a plant of the Figwort family (*Scrophulariaceae*) botanically known as *Pedicularis sceptrum-carolinum* L. This perennial herb is more than 1 m high and ranks among the most robust of European representatives of this species. The basal leaves are large, lanceolate, pinnately-lobed in a rosette. The stem is erect, tough, angular, hairless, with sparse opposite leaves, smaller than the basal leaves. One to three flowers in a sparse raceme grow from an axil of bracts. They have large (over 3 cm long) sulphur yellow corollas with a red stain on the bottom of the lip. They bloom from June to August.

The Moor-king is widespread in the northern part of Eurasia and in North America. In central Europe — on the south-western border of its range — it occurs as a relict from the ice age. It is absent from Britain. It grows on fens, in wet meadows or in birch groves. The creative protection of the Moor-king (as with other species of this family) — by means of the transfer of plants, sowing etc. — is very difficult. The *Pedicularis* species are semi-parasitic plants and live by extracting nutrients from the roots of neighbouring, host plants. This link complicates cultivation; however the problem is being addressed.

PEAT-BOGS, HEATHS

A typical north European raised peat-bog with a small lake in the Giant Mountains National Park, Bohemia.

The bog is a Nordic or Atlantic plant formation. The typical peat-bog in central Europe is found only in a relatively narrow zone on the North and Baltic Sea coasts from the most north-eastern part of France through Belgium, the Netherlands, Germany (in Upper Saxony, Schleswig Holstein and Mecklenburg-Vorpommern) and throughout Denmark. In northern Poland there are forest peat-bogs, most developed towards the east at the southern edge of the Eurasian taiga. In the south and south-east, into the interior of the continent, peat-bogs become a rarity. They are found as mountain peat-bogs in higher ranges: the Alps, the Carpathians, the Jura, the Vosges and the Schwarzland, in the Harz, the Thuringian Forest, the Fir Mountains, the Bohemian Forest, the Bavarian Forest, the Ore Mountains, the Giant Mountains, the Orlické and Jeseníky Mountains, also rarely on some lower highlands (the Rhone, the Czech-Moravian Highland).

There are extensive peat-bogs in both lowland and upland regions with higher rainfall in western Scotland, western Ireland and south-western Norway in particular.

Peat-bogs originate from specific natural conditions. In places with a positive water balance, in other words, where the total annual amount of rainfall exceeds the annual outflow and evaporation and where rain falls more or less regularly throughout the year, peat-moss (various species of *Sphagnum*) grows in abundance on marshland and creates peat-bogs. In view of the key role played in the formation of peat-bogs by rain water, this type of marsh is also called 'rain bog' or ombrogenous peat-bog.

The raised peat-bogs look like some sort of large concave lens. The peat mosses grow about 1 mm annually. Apart from cells for assimilation, their anatomic structure also contains large cells with water.

The peat moss cushion is like an enormous, water saturated mushroom. It can take in 15—30 times more water than its weight when dry. The entire peat-bog can be seen as one thick cushion of peat mosses covering an area of up to several square kilometres. The bottom parts of the peat moss clusters, with no access to light, die out. Under water with lack of oxygen, the imperfect decay of peat moss clusters and other plant remains occurs, the so-called 'peating' of peat soil, and this leads to the formation of peat. The peat can reach a thickness of up to twenty metres.

In an 'ideally' created raised peat-bog, in the middle of the 'lens' is a natural lake, the so-called eye, and closer to and round the edge there tend to be smaller water areas. The surface of the peat-bogs is a mosaic of elevated drier hillocks, so-called 'bults' and small depressions, permanently, or at least in certain seasons, flooded with water.

The peat-bog is a most distinct biotope. It is remarkable for its extreme dampness (however, for various reasons, it is not altogether accessible to higher plants, as it restricts their root systems), the clear lack of nutrients, especially nitrogen and the acid reaction of the soil. The flora is very symptomatic, adjusted to this habitat, but sparse in number. The centre of the peat-bog has no forest. The bults are overgrown with low small scrubs from the Heather family (*Ericaceae*), particularly of the *Vaccinium*, the heath (*Erica*) species and also members of the Crowberry family (*Empetraceae*). At the edges of pools and in depressions there are growths of numerous sedges (*Carex*), cotton grass (*Eriophorum*) and rushes (*Juncaceae*). The edges of raised peat-bogs are covered with trees — peat pine woods and dwarf pine in the mountains. As a consequence of the high content of water and the slow warming up of the soil, the raised peat-bog, at the beginning of the vegetation season, is a very cold habitat. This explains why on central European peat-bogs, we can find some clearly Nordic to Arctic relict plants and animals.

It is often claimed that raised peat-bogs in western and central Europe are one of the last remaining altogether natural, original ecosystems. This is true of many areas where the peat-bog has survived. There is constant discussion among water managers as to whether or not peat-bogs play a positive role in the overall hydrological regime of the countryside. Although no conclusions have been reached as yet, the fact remains that peat-bogs receive water, collect it and also systematically return it into circulation. Rivers which have their source in raised peat-bogs, have a balanced amount of water in wet, normal and drought years. Despite this, peat-bogs, particularly in lowlands, were considered as infertile land and many were drained and cultivated.

Many peat-bogs have been destroyed or significantly affected by peat cutting. Peat is, after all, an important raw material. Dry peat is flammable and was used extensively as fuel in the past. Special spades were used to carve out kinds of bricks, so-called peats which were dried and then used for fuel in households and factories. Today peat is more often used as a fertilizer in agriculture, vegetable growing and horticulture. It is humous and lightens the soil in mixtures and has a beneficial effect on the

◁ A tree-less mountain raised peat-bog in the inland of
▽ central Europe: Labrador Tea (*Ledum palustre*) shrubs in full bloom.

The Dwarf Cornel (*Cornus suecica*) is a woody sub- ▷ shrub relative of the bushy Dogwoods: the deceptive top flowers are in fact entire inflorescences with four large, purely white bracts.

The Cloudberry (*Rubus chamaemorus*) is a herbal ▷ relative of the Brambles bearing brownish orange ▽ edible fruit: it is picked in the north; in central and western Europe it is a very rare, strictly protected relict.

soil structure. Certain species of peat even have curative properties (peat spas with peat packs and baths).

There is one more important function fulfilled by peat. We can learn from peat-bogs how the surrounding countryside must have appeared long before the presence of man. In each layer of peat large numbers of pollen grains were stored mainly from the woody plants of the surrounding plant communities. Thanks to the special conditions (peat acts like a conservation agent), the pollen grains have been preserved and remained undisturbed. A very precise and detailed picture can be formed via the so-called pollen analysis, whereby the species and amount of pollen grains in peat are studied, of the evolution of European vegetation in the last geological period — the Quaternary.

The cutting, drainage and cultivation of European peat-bogs have also turned these ecological systems into endangered biotopes. The only chance of their survival is in those places where they are declared protected territories and therefore receive constant care.

Of the 209 species of vascular plants which are found on peat-bogs in the western part of Germany, 123 (58%) are on the red list, 7 are already extinct, 40 are endangered. For these ecologically highly specialized species there is virtually no substitute habitat. Fortunately raised peat-bogs communities can, to a certain extent, be naturally regenerated or artificially reconstructed on areas where peat has been cut but where the impermeable base has not been disturbed.

There are many fine peat-bogs in Scotland, some of them within protected areas. In England few lowland bogs remain intact. Reclamation for agriculture, some of it dating back to the early seventeenth century, has altered thousands of hectares of former peatland.

In costal north-western parts of Europe, i.e. in Denmark, Germany, the Netherlands and Belgium, France, Portugal, Norway and Britain, and more so in the Atlantic rather than the Baltic region, peat-bog communities pervade communities of heaths in lowland areas. Heaths are relatively monotonous, but develop very effective (particularly during

the flowering period in late summer) growths of small low scrubs of the heath genus. The Heather (*Calluna vulgaris* L.) predominates on drier sites and the Cross-leaved Heath (*Erica tetralix* L.) on the damp sites. In the open countryside heathland was restricted, so it is often found there in temporary communities. Heathlands originated in the late Middle Ages on the site of felled trees and survived thanks to traditional land cultivation. However, with modern farming and afforestation methods, the area has diminished considerably since the nineteenth century. Only in some of the most exposed areas of south-western England and south-western Ireland

can heathland be considered to be the natural vegetation. The remaining larger heaths are protected today in various categories of protected areas. They are preserved in the best possible way by the 'artificial' continuation of traditional land cultivation methods. However in recent years the heather has been declining. It would appear that air pollution is causing most of the damage with the infamous 'acid rain'. A good example of all aspects of this 'heath' problem is the biggest heath Nature Reserve with an area of 200 square kilometres, the Lüneburger Heide in Germany, which bears a European Council diploma.

In western and central Europe the **Dwarf Cornel** (*Cornus suecica* L.) of the Dogwood family (*Cornaceae*) is a great rarity. We mostly think of dogwood as a shrub. The Dwarf Cornel is, however, a perennial herb only 5 to 25 cm in height with distinct four-angled erect stems. It is a highly conspicuous plant when in flower and bearing fruit. The cymous inflorescence at the end of the stem is made up of a number of small dark-red to reddish-violet flowers. The entire inflorescence is supported by four large pure white oval bracts 1 to 2 cm long. The bracts resemble petals and the entire structure looks like one large 'flower'. The fruit is a bright coral red drupe. The plants blossom in May and the fruit ripens in the summer.

The Dwarf Cornel is a Nordic to Arctic plant. It is quite common in damp, light forests and thickets in Norway, Sweden and Finland, and in northern regions of the European part of Russia and can be seen on the northern coasts of the Baltic Sea. However, it is a rarity on the southern Baltic coast. It grows there on peat soils in the communities of low shrubs of the *Vaccinium* species, Crowberry (*Empetrum nigrum* L.) and the Cross-leaved Heath (*Erica tetralix* L.) etc. It is no longer found in eastern Germany and it is doubtful whether it grows there any more. It was also recorded in the area surrounding Gdansk (Danzig) in Poland. On the south-western border of its range it penetrates England and the Netherlands. The last certain but very scattered occurrences are in Lower Saxony and Schleswig-Holstein in Germany and in Denmark. In Scotland the Dwarf Cornel is still not uncommon, especially on the islands; it occupies localised habitats in England north of Lancashire and Yorkshire. It is widely cultivated in gardens in Britain.

The **Cloudberry** (*Rubus chamaemorus* L.) of the Rose family (*Rosaceae*) is also a species of the far north. This species differs from most other representatives of its genus because it is a perennial herb only 5 to 25 cm high. The glandular, hairy, unbranched stem is covered with several alternating leaves with long leafstalks and simple, kidney-shaped, shallow five to seven-lobed blades with cre-

Distribution of the Cloudberry in Europe.

The Bog Rosemary (*Andromeda polifolia*) has bell- ▷ shaped flowers in a terminal corymb which resemble delicate, small, pink flasks: the grey leaves with the margin rolled under contain a strong poison.

The Labrador Tea (*Ledum palustre*), with its balls of ▷ ▽ white flowers, is a characteristic species of peat-bogs: however, it also grows in Czech-Saxony-Switzerland on steep sandstone rocks, as shown in the picture taken at the Elbe canyon.

nate and serrate edges. The individual flowers on the end of the stems are long-stalked, five-part and white measuring over 2 cm in diameter. They flower at the end of spring — in May and June. The fruit — the blackberries or brambles — are large and conspicuous, ripening at the end of summer. First they are purple and swollen, orange-red and yellow-orange when ripe and brown when overripe.

The Cloudberry is a circumpolar plant in the Earth's sub-Arctic to Arctic zone. It reaches the 80° northern latitude (on the Spitzbergen islands). It is a very common species of peat-bogs where it grows in peat-moss cushions. The most southern European locations, just as with the Swedish Dogwood, are of a clearly relict character. On the typical raised peat-bogs in the north-western part of Germany the Cloudberry has still survived in a few places in Lower Saxony and in Schleswig-Holstein. Once it probably also grew on the Darss peninsula in Mecklenburg-Vorpommern, but today there is no trace of it there. Due to its rarity it is strictly protected in the reserve of the forest raised peat-bog in the Polish Biosphere Reserve of the Slowinski National Park not far from Leba. It might also be found on raised peat-bogs in the Black Forest. Today however it survives on the upland peat-bogs of the Giant Mountains in the belt of dwarf pines where it flowers and bears fruit in abundance. It is listed as the most important Czech glacial relict and its sites — just as in Germany and Poland — are strictly protected in nature reserves. In Britain, Cloudberry is quite abundant in some areas of the Scottish Highlands. From there it also extends to northern England and Wales. It is very rare in Ireland, and found in the north only.

The entire Cloudberry plant has a pleasant scent resembling that of carnations. The fruit is edible and very tasty. It contains 3 to 6% sugar and a large amount of citric and apple acid. On northern upland peat-bogs wild animals — bears, reindeer and hares — like to eat the Cloudberry. It is also picked in abundance by people but obviously only in areas where it is widespread. In folk medicine the Cloudberry was used for treating scurvy. In nordic European countries the fruit of the cloudberry is sold in summer for cloudberry or mixed fruit salads. One of the Finnish export specialities is sweet liquor prepared from the Cloudberry.

Similar to the Cloudberry, but with 3-lobed or ternate leaves and bright reddish-pink flowers, is the **Arctic Bramble** (*Rubus arcticus* L.). Fruit of this species is dark red when ripe. As the name indicates, the Arctic Bramble is spread even farther to the north, its European occurrence restricted to Scandinavia, Finland, northern Russia and rarely Estonia, where it grows on moors and also in grassy places and thickets. Its geographical range originally included Britain with three or four areas of occurrence in the Scottish Highlands. It has not been seen there, however, since the beginning of the last century. So the Arctic Bramble is extinct in Britain.

In Greek mythology Andromeda became the wife of Perseus after he saved her when she was helplessly chained to a rock on a sea coast to face the monster called Kethos. Then after her death, Andromeda became a goddess. The myths about her were the inspiration for numerous art works. The constellation of the autumn sky was named after her and even an interesting plant — the **Bog Rosemary** (*Andromeda polifolia* L.) of the Heather family (*Ericaceae*). It does not grow, however, on rocky sea coats but on upland peat-bogs. It does not require help against sea monsters, but protection against peat cutting, drainage, artificial fertilization and other effects of civilization. In Europe it is now on red lists and in many countries (Slovakia, France, Austria) also on the lists of protected plants.

It is a dwarf evergreen shrub measuring 10 to 30 cm. Due to its linear, lanceolate leaves with narrowly rolled under margins, dark-green on the front and whitish-grey beneath, it is popularly called in German the 'wild rosemary'. The leaves are 1—3 cm wide, and alternate on ascendant slightly branched

stems, which grow from creeping, woody rhizomes. There are 1 to 4 flowers at the end of corymbs on long (3 to 4 cm), reddish stalks. The flowers are about 0.5 cm long. They look like pale pink balls with short, rolled back lobes at the mouth. They bloom at the end of spring — from May to June. The fruit is a bluish-green globular capsule.

The Bog Rosemary is a Nordic species, characteristic of a number of peat-bog plant communities with the predominating peat-mosses — *Sphagnetalia*. In western and central Europe it is found on raised peat-bogs — from the typical raised peat-bogs in the north German lowland to highlands inland where it grows to 1,500 m above sea level. In Britain it is confined to central and northern England, as well as southern and central Scotland, but it is absent from the Scottish Highlands. It also occurs in Ireland. It has been much reduced by habitat loss. The leaves of this herb contain the poison andrometoxin.

Another more robust plant of the same Heather family (*Ericaceae*) has also earned itself the German folk name 'wild rosemary'. It is the evergreen shrub **Labrador Tea** (*Ledum palustre* L.), a very close relative of the Alpenroses (*Rhododendron*). It grows to a height of 50 cm to 1.5 m. It is an erect, abundantly branched shrub. The young twigs are thick and hairy. The dense leaves on the end of the branches are linear to narrowly lanceolate, tough and leathery with rolled under margins and tomentose on the back. The large 5-part flowers with pure white petals (1 to 1.5 cm long) are grouped into dense, globular to elongated umbels. They appear from May to July according to their habitat. The Labrador Tea is rich in flowers so it is a very attractive bush, particularly in May.

The entire plant is strongly aromatic. It was formerly used as an insect repellent. The Labrador Tea contains a number of interesting chemical substances. The leaves contain essence and the poison ledol. The Labrador Tea is a potentially useful and valuable plant, given its content of these substances, although they have not yet been fully investigated. In some central European countries such as Germany, it is still on the official list of medicinal plants. The dried upper part is used with leaves and flowers — Herba et Folia Ledi palustris. The drug has calming to narcotic effects. It is used for treating coughs (particularly choking and whooping coughs), diarrhoea, rheumatism and skin diseases. The Labrador Tea was formerly used with considerable risk as an abortion drug and in brewing as a substitute for hops.

The shrub is also cultivated in gardens for its decorative appearance — particularly in rock gardens and at the edge of ponds, although its use in this respect is restricted due to its habitat requirements. It requires sufficient air humidity and acid peat soil with a rich content of raw humus. It is a strict calcifuge. The Labrador Tea is a plant which likes partial shade, but it is found growing in open areas just as often as in the shaded depths of gorges. The width and the revolute structure of its leaves alter depending on the amount of light it receives.

The Labrador Tea is a Nordic to Arctic circumpolar species. In northern Eurasia it is found commonly on peat-bogs and in bog forests where it creates entire growths (just as bilberries do in coniferous forests) in the undergrowth of a certain type of the Eurasian taiga. Its south-western border

Distribution of the Labrador Tea in Europe.

of geographical growth runs across central Europe.

The main central European habitat of the Labrador Tea is boggy pine woods — the plant association *Ledo-Pinetum*, which belongs to the communities endangered in central Europe. The species is protected by law in all the central European countries where it occurs. Many nature reserves have been set up in central Europe for securing the conservation of the species and the communities which are characteristic for this species. A successful outcome has been achieved in these reserves as far as the spontaneous regeneration of the *Ledum* population is concerned on formerly cut peat deposits, for example in the South Bohemian Biosphere Reserve and Protected Landscape Area Třeboň Region. However despite this the Labrador Tea is on the decline in the south-western part of its range and is marked as a threatened species on red lists, in some cases as a missing or even extinct species.

An interesting region in the central European interior where the Labrador Tea does grow in abundance, is the bilateral park of 'Bohemian-Saxonian Switzerland'. The Labrador Tea grows there on sandstone rocks, i.e. in what at first sight appear to be untypical habitats for it. However, a detailed study has shown that basically identical conditions exist in those rock habitats as in the raised peat-bogs.

A species very like the Labrador Tea, but with narrower, more elliptic leaves, with the midrib concealed below, is the **Greenland Labrador Tea** (*Ledum groenlandicum* Oeder). Sometimes considered only as a subspecies of *Ledum palustre*, it grows in similar habitats. Greenland Labrador Tea is a British Red Data Book plant. It is believed to be native in bogs in one area of Perthshire in Scotland.

As stated at the beginning of this chapter, many plant species typical of raised peat-bogs are rather inconspicuous and grass-like in appearance with small flowers, and they are easily confused. However, there are exceptions in terms of attractiveness and these are plants of the Sedge family (*Cyperaceae*) of Cottongrass (*Eriophorum*) genus with their whitish 'cotton' tufts of hair in the spikelets. The **Hare's-tail Cottongrass** (*Eriophorum vaginatum* L.), typical of the raised peat-bogs, and the rarer Arctic-Alpine (Alps, Carpathians) *Eriophorum scheuchzeri* Hoppe have a single spikelet, therefore a single cotton tuft. The more common **Broad-leaved Cottongrass** (*Eriophorum latifolium* Hoppe) and the **Common Cottongrass** (*Eriophorum angustifolium* Honck) have several nodding and long-stalked spikelets.

Among the rarest and most endangered is the

66

◁ The small Alpine Deergrass (*Trichophorum alpinum*) is a miniature form of the Cottongrass (*Eriophorum*) which is about 0.25 m high. Its experimental protective cultivation has been started at the Serrahn Nature Reserve in eastern Germany.

◁ The White Beak-sedge (*Rhynchospora alba*), a plant of
▽ the Sedge family (*Cyperaceae*) with whitish yellow terminal clusters of spikelets, is perfectly inconspicuous in its appearance, but it is a significant characteristic phytosociological species, indicator and endangered species.

The Rannoch Rush (*Scheuchzeria palustris*) is an incon- ▷
spicuous, tiny, grass-like herb: the leek-like leaves exceed the raceme in length with several small flowers in the axil of greenish bracts.

The Bog Asphodel (*Narthecium ossifragum*) has grass- ▷
like leaves and clear green perianths which are yellow ▽
inside. This species of transient peat-bogs grows in acid soils, sunny habitats and cannot tolerate grazing.

triangular stemmed arctic-alpine **Slender Cottongrass** (*Eriophorum gracile* Koch) which is on the European red list.

This species is also included in the British Red Data Book. Since 1960 it has been recorded only in Hampshire, Surrey, Glamorgan and Gwynedd; it is apparently extinct in Somerset, Northamptonshire, Yorkshire, Dorset and Norfolk. In Ireland it was discovered as late as 1966, but it is undoubtedly native there. This is a very difficult species to preserve. As it requires extremely wet conditions, it is very vulnerable to drainage and reclamation.

A smaller 'double' of the Cottongrass are the Deergrasses (*Trichophorum*). The **Alpine Deergrass** (*Trichophorum alpinum* (L.) Pers.) is a perennial greyish green sparsely tufted herb measuring 10 to 30 cm. The triangular stem has a coarse single floral spikelet at the end (it flowers from April to May) and after blooming it has a 2 cm long tuft of white hairs.

The Alpine Deergrass is a rare nordic plant. In central Europe it is sparsely scattered in northern lowlands, highlands, foothills and mountains (in the Alps up to an altitude of over 1,800 metres above sea level). It grows in specific habitats in depressions or on the flooded perimeters of typical and upland peat-bogs and transitional peat-bogs. It can also be found in rich mineral soils in the communities of Davall sedge. These habitats are sensitive to human management of the countryside and in many places populations of species found on some central European red lists in the highest threat categories have survived only thanks to traditional methods of extensive use of acid peat and marsh meadows. It appears that so far no serious risk threatens the Alpine Deergrass in the Alps. Elsewhere it only has a real chance of surviving in well-managed nature reserves.

A genus of inconspicuous, grassy, sparsely tufted perennials (only about 0.25 m high) belonging to the sedge family (*Cyperaceae*), which is characteristic of certain types of peat-bogs, is the **Beak-sedge** (*Rhynchospora*). Two species can be found in central and western Europe.

The **White Beak-sedge** (*Rhynchospora alba* (L.) Vahl) is a perennial light green herb. The erect stems with narrow linear leaves grow from a creeping rhizome. The small spikelets make up a sparse cluster of two to three flowers with a longer supporting bract. The perianth bracteoles are yellowish or greenish white and later pinkish. The plant blooms from June to August.

The White Beak-sedge is a circumpolar northern species. In central Europe it is found in raised peat-bogs and transitional peat-bogs. It grows most often in flooded depressions and shallow pools together with some species of peat-moss. It is the predominant species of plant communities from the union of *Rhynchosporion albae* which is disappearing in central and western Europe. It is found on some European red lists in various threat categories, but not in Britain, where it has a fairly wide distribution.

The **Brown Beak-sedge** (*Rhynchospora fusca* (L.) Ait.) is

Distribution of the Bog Asphodel in Europe.

▽ The Bog Orchid (*Hammarbya paludosa*) can easily be overlooked growing among cushions of peat-moss on very damp, permanently flooded sites: the long and narrow inflorescence is composed of tiny, yellowish-green flowers with the lip turned upwards.

The Round-leaved Sundew (*Drosera rotundifolia*) has ▷ longstalked leaves growing in basal rosettes and rounded leaf blades covered by sticky hairs with dew-tipped 'sundew-drops': it has been destroyed in many sites by herbalists because it was thought that it possessed a miraculous curative power.

more rare in Britain than the above species. Confined to southern and western England and Ireland it was considered for inclusion in the British Red Data Book, but ultimately discarded. It differs from *Rhynchospora alba* in its dark yellow and red-brown bracteoles.

The small but conspicuous **Rannoch Rush** (*Scheuchzeria palustris* L.) is also of scientific interest in the raised peat-bogs. It belongs to the *Scheuchzeriaceae* family which contains only one genus. Until recently it was thought that this genus had only one species; today some botanists distinguish the American specimens as a different one. The Rannoch Rush is a circumpolar species occurring in a relatively narrow strip in the north of the temperate zone, on the coasts of Eurasia and Greenland, in Iceland and in a narrow strip crossing North America between the 50° and 60° parallels of the northern latitude.

It is a short, 10 to 25 cm, perennial with erect, sparsely branched, herbaceous stems and linear, trough-shaped leaves as in rush. The bottom parts of the stems and the slanting, protruding rhizome are covered by sheaths of dead leaves. The small yellowish green flowers with petals compose a raceme of few flowers. They bloom at the end of spring — in May and June—and in the summer fruit can be seen: three inflated orbicular follicles about 0.5 cm long, fused at the base.

From its nordic range the Rannoch Rush descends to western and central Europe where it is on red lists in the highest threat categories. This inconspicuous and rare species is so significant that an entire class of plant associations has been named after it — the *Scheuchzerio-Cariceteae fuscae* and a number of communities of raised peat-bog depressions and transitional flooded peat-bogs — the *Scheuchzerietalia palustris*.

All formerly recorded populations of Rannoch Rush in northern England (Shropshire, Cheshire, Yorkshire) and also many in Scotland (Inverness-shire and Argyllshire) have been eliminated through drainage, peat cutting and afforestation. The Rannoch Rush is now confined to two small areas in Perthshire and is entered in the British Red Data Book. Not long ago (1951) it was first located in Ireland, but the bog habitat was drained and it became extinct very soon after its discovery.

The acid raised peat-bogs and heaths which are low in nutrients also have their 'lilies'. The next plant belongs to the Lily family (*Liliaceae*). It is called the **Bog Asphodel** (*Narthecium ossifragum* (L.) Huds.)

In Europe it is a very interesting species for linguists. Its official name in several languages means 'bone-breaker', which is certainly unusual. It derives from the folk belief that cattle often break their legs after eating this plant. However, it also has the old folk name of 'leg-healer' as, after rubbing injured limbs with the juice of this herb, the injury healed quickly. The north German folk name of 'Schusterknef' — the Shoemaker's Knife — was inspired by the shape of the leaves. The English name indicates its similarity to true Asphodels (*Asphodelus*), Mediterranean flowering beauties appreciated in horticulture.

The Bog Asphodel is a perennial, 10 to 40 cm high herb with a creeping, thin, branched rhizome and erect simple stems. The leaves are linear, erect, greyish green, 5—10 cm long, somewhat sword-shaped so they resemble the leaves of the iris. The flowers grow on the end of the stem in a raceme which is 6 to 8 cm long. The perianth parts (petals), about 0.75 cm long, are greenish on

Distribution of the Common Sundew in Europe.

the outside and bright yellow inside. The plant blooms in July and August and sometimes in September.

The remarkable contents of this herb are the subject of research. The flowers give off a pleasant scent resembling the scent of the wild European Butterfly Orchid (*Platanthera bifolia*). The plant is poisonous and no reports exist to indicate that it has ever been collected as a medicinal plant.

The Bog Asphodel is a typical Atlantic species. It grows well in the oceanic climate of western and north-western Europe from the Iberian peninsula to Scandinavia. It is generally widespread in Britain with the exception of eastern England and is reported to occur in the more southern parts of Baltic states. Hence some botanists speak of it as a northern oceanic species.

Due to its decorative appearance the Bog Asphodel is cultivated as an ornamental flower. Cultivators of botanical species of native European orchids have found a special use for this plant in the last decades. In order to copy a natural biotope, cultivators require a 'lawn' for their orchids. The real species of grass for this purpose are unsuitable for the competitively weak orchids and so lawns of the Bog Asphodel are being used successfully.

In the wild the Bog Asphodel also often creates thick and extensive grasslike growths. Moreover, it is a pioneer plant, colonizing naked peat soils as the first vascular plant. It is a species of raised heath bogs characteristic for the plant communities union of *Ericion tetralicis* (with the Cross-leaved Heather), the so-called damp heath.

We have already mentioned orchids. As a result of the large number of members of the Orchid family (*Orchidaceae*) every tenth, possibly even every ninth plant species on Earth is an orchid. So even raised

peat-bogs are not without orchids. However in order to discover any, we often need good eye-sight and a lot of luck. The typical highland peat-bog **Bog Orchid** (*Hammarbya paludosa* (L.) O.Kuntze) is the smallest wild European orchid. (The scientific name was derived from the Swedish Hammarby estate which was bought by the father of systematic botany, Carolus Linnaeus.) It grows to a height of only 5 to 15 cm and rarely to 20 cm. It is characterised – as are other peat-bog herbs – by its growth in 'floors' to keep up with the peat-moss in whose cushions it is found. The new bulbils of this perennial grow in the axil of the highest leaf. There are ususally two to three leaves of about 1 to 2.5 cm in length and over 0.5 cm wide. They are situated at the base of the stem. The inflorescence is very long and narrow. The tiny yellowish green flowers are remarkable morphologically speaking because the lip (without a spur) is situated in their upper section. The Bog Orchid flowers in July and August. Later the tiniest seeds (about 0.2 mm) to be found in European orchids, ripen in its capsules.

The Bog Orchid is a Eurasian species with oceanic and Nordic distribution trends. However, in its relatively extensive area of growth, it has never been abundant; moreover in recent decades many known areas of occurrence have disappeared. In Belgium, France, Germany and Switzerland it is an endangered species. The Bog Orchid is on the European red list. It was considered for inclusion in the British Red Data Book, but has been discarded because it still occurs in numerous localities in bogs in the north and west of Britain and in a few places in Ireland. It is declining however in south and east England. It is protected by law in Germany, but effective protection of special biotopes where the Bog Orchid is found is contributing greatly to its preservation.

The habitats of this rare and endangered species are raised peat-bogs and transitional peat-bogs where it grows in flooded depressions and cushions of peat-moss, often together with the Beak Sedge as the characteristic species of the union of *Rhynchosporion albae*.

For experts the Bog Orchid still bears a lot of secrets as to its life and development. So far neither in natural nor in artificial conditions has it been possible to observe the generative propagation of the species (from the seeds). This plant breeds vegetatively by creating bulbils on the leaves. It is a unique phenomenon among native European orchids.

The **Marsh Orchids** (*Dactylorhiza*) are a more frequent sight on peat-bogs with wide, hand-like tubers and leafy stems of more than 0.5 m in height, with dense or sparse spikes of medium-sized flowers. The **Common Spotted Orchid (** *Dactylorhiza fuchsii* (Druce) Soo), is widespread in Eurasia, whereas the **Heath Spotted Orchid (** *Dactylorhiza maculata* (L.) Soo) is less widespread than was previously supposed. A rare and problematical plant is the **Narrow-leaved Marsh Orchid** (*Dactylorhiza traunsteineri* (Sauter) Soo). All these Marsh Orchids occur in Britain. They are not yet regarded as endangered; the Narrow-leaved Marsh Orchid was under consideration for the British Red Data Book, but was ultimately discarded. But these interesting plants and their habitats need to be preserved.

A true legend of the raised peat-bogs are the **Sundews** (*Drosera*) of the Sundew family (*Droseraceae*). Every nature lover longs to see a sundew plant when visiting a raised peat-bog (popular nature trails cross many peat-bogs in Europe). However, not everyone can, even though they may almost trample over the plant. The sundews are very small and with their reddish colour they often almost disappear in the red and brown peat-moss cushions. The Sundew family includes carnivorous plants which in their habitats, mostly poor in nitrogen, improve their nourishment by trapping and digesting small insects. (Small pieces of cheese can also be used if experimenting in the 'feeding' of the *Drosera*.) Hence their leaves act like 'traps'. They are covered with glandular hairs. At the end of the hairs there is a drop of sticky mucus which the plant uses for trapping and, thanks to its chemical composition, also for digesting insects (this is the so-called 'sun dew' in the German and English name for the plant). The leaves, particularly the young ones, roll up at the same time.

European Sundew family members are perennial herbs. Scapes carrying lax spikes of small, whitish, 5-part flowers grow from ground leaf-rosettes. The sundews flower in summer from June to August. When in flower they grow to a height of 5 to 15, at most 30 cm.

The most abundant among the European species is the **Round-leaved Sundew** (*Drosera rotundifolia* L.). As the species name indicates, it has rounded leaf blades about 1 cm in diameter with long stalks. The entire leaf-rosette sometime does not even reach 2 cm in diameter. The flower bearing scapes are two to four times longer than the leaves.

The Round-leaved Sundew is a medicinal plant. Since ancient times it has been used for its almost magical, universal power in folk medicine: 'A person stricken by a heart attack, after drinking the juice of sundew, will begin to speak and walk, even though that person may have been completely paralysed. But this elixir will immediately dispel all faintness and fatigue.' Perhaps the 'dew' on leaves glistening in the sun's rays instilled in people some sort of belief in its miraculous effects. Herbalists prescribed the sun-

dew to people with tuberculosis and other lung ailments. Even today a drug made from the plant's stems (*Herba droserae*) is used for relieving muscle cramp and for removal of phlegm. It also has various other beneficial effects. It is interesting that, despite long research, it has not yet been established what sort of main effective substances this herb does contain.

Once it was thought that with intensive collecting the sundew would become extinct in central Europe. Today it is protected by law (the drug is imported into central European countries) but despite this, it is listed as a threatened species and is really declining. Of course the reason for this is not due to the fact that it has been collected so much, but due to the destruction of its bog habitats. The most typical habitats are peat-bogs, but the sundew can also be found in fens and other wet meadows, on wet rocks and flushes (in the mountains up to an altitude of about 1,500 metres above sea level), or even in damp heaths and sands. It is widespread in the northern hemisphere. Attempts at cultivating the Round-leaved Sundew on medicinal plantations have proved unsuccessful so far.

The **Great Sundew** (*Drosera anglica* Huds.), as opposed to the previous species, has narrow oblong leaves with blades up to 4 cm and the flower bearing scapes are shorter than the leaves. It is an altogether rarer plant even in the north. Ecologically speaking it is specialized as a characteristic species of the order of plant associations called *Scheuchzerietalia palustris* in flooded depressions and smaller raised peat-bog pools.

A sort of 'inter-species' between the above two is the **Long-leaved Sundew** (*Drosera intermedia* Hayne.). It is an even rarer species because it has a north-suboceanic trend and is rarely found in cen-

tral Europe. It has an even greater ecological specialization, and grows on bare, constantly or occasionally flooded acid, mineral, (sandy) soils, which are low in nutrients as well as on peaty swamps and in the dampest peat-moss cushions. The *Drosera obovata* Mert et W. O. G. Koch, which resembles this species to a certain extent, is a hybrid between the *Drosera rotundifolia* and the *Drosera anglica*.

Raised peat-bogs also have their characteristic cryptogams. On raised peat-bogs one often finds the Royal Fern. Of the variety of Clubmosses (*Lycopodiaceae*) the most significant inhabitant of peat-bogs is the **Marsh Clubmoss** (*Lycopodiella inundata* (L.) Holub.). It is a creeping perennial scarcely branched, up to 10 cm high. The stems are densely covered by subulate, linear leaves, whereas fruiting spikes on erect branches are difficult to distinguish from sterile parts.

This rare and threatened species is a circumpolar plant with a certain nordic-subatlantic trend and is sometimes found in Europe today on flooded mineral and peaty but always acid soils, in heathy bogs and sandy swamps growing from the lowlands to the mountains up to 1,500 m above sea level. This is another case where the plant depends on the protection of its biotopes for its survival.

ROCKS, ROCKY STEPPES, CONTINENTAL WARM SANDS

The natural rocky outcrops are hosts to rare flora of various origins with numerous relicts from earlier periods of development of vegetation.

One of the most important biomes — i.e. ecological systems with uniform characteristic vegetation over extensive areas — is the steppe. In Eurasia, the steppe zone stretches from the foothills of the central Asian high mountains to the southern extremities of the Urals and from there across the Volga basin to the Black Sea between the forest steppe and semi-desert zone. In places this zone is over 500 kilometres wide. In central Europe — in other words outside the actual steppe zone — islands have developed of diverse plant communities which are either identical to the steppe communities or very similar. In their composition they have many remarkable, attractive and rare plant species, so that they have long enjoyed the great attention and favour of professional and amateur botanists and later obviously became the subject of high priority nature conservation interests.

The essential characteristic of the steppe is its lack of woodland. Its plant communities are mainly made up of herbs (and if these are woody plants, then only low in growth) and grasses tend to predominate among them. This state is conditioned by the small amount of annual rainfall (300 to 500 mm) which does not allow the existence of natural woodland. Individual species of steppe plants are adjusted in various ways to these climatic conditions. These are so-called geophytes — plants with underground organs (bulbs, tubers, rhizomes) which enable them to live through the unfavourable, dry season. The deep roots and the more extensive root system supply them with sufficient moisture. Various adaptations (hairs, reduction in the surface of the leaves for the price of slower growth, fleshy stems and leaves) limit the output of water through stem.

How come that these species and their entire communities are found in central and partly even western Europe which is mostly a woodland region? The central European extra-zone steppes are not primarily conditioned by the climate. As a further factor the local climate or microclimate (regions in the rain shadow of range of mountains, on steep, south facing, sunny and dry slopes) contribute to their origin and existence. These plant formations are more usually conditioned by the soils because they are found on very shallow, primitive soils, on rocky outcrops where the competition of more demanding species is strongly restricted. We are talking about so-called rocky steppes which are the subject of scientific interest in central and western Europe. Rocks in central and western Europe are the habitats of many interesting species, often relicts of steppe, xerophilous and thermophilous in character. In some places remarkable endemic species have developed, particularly on areas of ground with very specialised characteristics (such as serpentines).

Experts constantly debate or even dispute issues concerning central European steppes, their origin, development and prospects. These plant formations are so diverse and vary so much from one case to another, that only certain basic and common features can be distinguished, which simplify any descriptions.

To a considerable extent man has also contributed and is contributing to central and western European steppe communities, their origin and existence. The felling of forests in certain locations could have led to the development of grasslands and open communities of herbs which, in their structure and appearance, resemble steppes. Certain farming methods, particularly the grazing of domestic animals, support the maintenance of these forest free communities.

Scattered throughout central and even western

Europe are various sized islands of distinctive flora and vegetation which botanists describe as xerotherm flora and vegetation. These are plants which are resistant to drought (sometimes they are also, and not altogether accurately, called xerophilous) and with certain warmth requirements (thermophilous). After the ice age such plants extended in growth, often with contribution from human activities, in warm Alpine valleys (in the Valais Alps in Switzerland up to a height of about 2,000 m above sea level), on the southern slopes of foothills and hills, particularly on limestone or igneous rock (in the Frankish Jura, the Kyffhäuser in Germany, Bohemian karst, the Cracow-Czestochowa Highland, the German, Austrian, Hungarian and Czech and Slovak headlands and the foothills of the Alps and Carpathians, etc.) and to steep and sunny valley slopes of big rivers and their tributaries (the Rhine, Danube, Oder, Vltava etc.). Similar communities also inhabit warm and sandy regions, e.g. in the Rhineland, the Elbe Basin, the Oder Basin and the Vistula Basin, the Morava Basin and the Danubian Basin.

The species composition of these communities is a very diverse one. The individual species are of various origin. Some originate from real steppe and forest regions in the Pannonian Lowland and near the Black Sea (the Pannonian and Pontic species). Others have descended from mountains at a certain period in the evolution of central European flora and vegetation (de-Alpine). Species are also found here which have as their main range the south European (Mediterranean) region. Some species come from western Europe. Many of them are ornamental rock plants and are cultivated as such. Unfortunately people collect and uproot them for this purpose in the wild and transfer them to gardens.

However, the worst of the negative human influences against which the diverse flora of European rocky steppes and warm sands has to be protected is the habitat destruction leading to the collapse of interesting ecosystems. This may come about through direct intervention such as the opening of a quarry in a rocky mountain side. Of course sometimes a derelict quarry may provide these plants with a substitute habitat. A more dangerous action is the flooding of rocky steppes with a lake created in a river valley by the construction of a dam. However even an indirect action can cause substantial damage. For example, the afforestation of these habitats in central Europe with exotic False Acacia (*Robinia pseudacacia*) and Black Pine (*Pinus nigra*) has proved greatly damaging. In the undergrowth of newly planted forests and groves, the diverse xerotherm flora and vegetation has been almost completely suppressed. The struggle against acacia trees, which are firmly rooted or

74

Distribution of the Golden Alyssum in Europe.

spread to these habitats from surrounding areas, is one of the great problems facing central European protected areas with xerotherm ecosystems.

The most important examples of these plant communities in central Europe are found today in a representative network of reserves and other protected areas.

The **Golden Alyssum** (*Alyssum saxatile* L.) is exclusively a rock plant. As indicated by its 4-part flowers with pale to richly golden-yellow petals of small but dense racemose inflorescence, Alyssum belongs to the Cress family (*Coniferae*). The stems grow from a rosette of ground leaves, the stems being 10 to 30 cm high. The leaves are up to 10 cm long and a greyish colour because they are densely covered by hairs.

The robust clusters of Golden Alyssum with

a woody root and basal stem are often of a semi-shrub character. The furcately branched roots are firmly anchored in the rocky crevices. The roots often penetrate the fissures in rocks filled with fertile humus and fine soil, which provides a sufficient amount of moisture, several metres deep. The Golden Alyssum usually grows in large populations on rocky walls and rocky hill-sides often in the steepest, most inaccessible places. The plants are attractive during flowering at the end of April and in May. 'The gold of the Alyssum is already trickling down the rocks . . .' according to the description of the Czech poet and Nobel Prize laureate, Jaroslav Seifert.

The Alisons (*Alyssum* genus) have a core of their geographiclal distribution in southern Europe — the Mediterranean. In the eastern area of its range the Golden Alyssum reaches central Europe. It is not particularly demanding of its ground properties, growing as well on limestone as on acid shale.

The Golden Alyssum, being a very decorative flower, is cultivated frequently in rock gardens, in stone walls and terraces. From there it often spreads, so it is sometimes difficult to ascertain the origin of its occurrence. As a threatened plant, it is found on many central European red lists. In Britain too the Golden Alyssum is a popular garden flower, and although not native, it has been naturalized in many places.

In Germany the smaller but also perennial **Mountain Alison** (*Alyssum montanum* L.) is a protected species with the centre of its range in south Europe. It is a plant without a ground leaf-rosette, with dense leaves on creeping to ascendant stems, partly sterile and partly carrying simple racemes of yellow flowers. The Mountain Alison is also a rock species, but occurs on less steep rock habitats, often on flat places with a shallow layer of soil or on scree. It is also a species of warm regions, a pioneer of rock

◁ Contrary to its name, the Bohemian Gagea (*Gagea bohemica*) grows in shallow soils of rocky habitats throughout Europe from Turkey to Wales.

The Yellow Pheasant's-eye (*Adonis vernalis*) is found in ▷ the warmest regions of central and south-western Eu- ▽ rope, on the border of its range occurring sporadically on rocky steppes, dry grasslands, forest steppes and open woods. Its large, decorative flowers open only on sunny days.

The Hoary Rockrose (*Helianthemum canum*) has leaves ▷ which are hairy on the upperside and on the margins, and white tomentose on the underside: it is an exclusively calciphilous species.

and scree plant communities, but is more selective in soil than the previous species. It often grows on limestone and base-rich ingeous rocks. It is also a decorative rock plant, but is not so widely cultivated in gardens. The **Small Alison** (*Alyssum alyssoides* (L.) L.) is a low, greyish annual or biennial with small lanceolate leaves and dense raceme of pale yellow flowers with slightly notched petals. It grows throughout Europe from Scandinavia to the Caucasus, but is very rare in Britain, growing there on lowland sandy and calcareous grassy fields and lands very localised in south and east England and east Scotland. It is a protected species included in the British Red Data Book.

A tiny, but very charming plant can be discovered growing on an early spring rocky steppe. It resembles a miniature tulip and is called **Bohemian Gagea** (*Gagea bohemica* (Zauschner) Regel et Schmahl) of the Lily family (*Liliaceae*). It is a perennial herb with underground bulbs from which grow thread-like, only 0.5 to 1 mm wide, rounded, bluish-green leaves and 1–3 flowers, sometimes up to 1 cm long with six yellow petals. The Bohemian Gagea flowers from March to April, so that there is no longer any sign of this small, beautiful flower in late spring.

It is a European species growing mainly in southern Europe. In central and western Europe it is sometimes found in rocky steppes in overground open pioneer plant communities together with dwarf speedwells and stonecrops. It grows on poor quartz to acidic and lime-free ground. In Bohemia, the country it is named after, it is an officially protected species and listed in the highest threat category.

In Britain the Bohemian Gagea was first found in 1965, but due to a wrong determination recognized only in 1974 as a native member of the British flora. The rocky habitat lies in the mid-Wales, fortunately in the National Nature Reserve. The specimens there are nearly always single-flowered, ascribed to the subspecies *gallica* (Rovy) J.B.K. Richardson, with silky basal leaves with whitish hairs. This subspecies also grows in western France. The Bohemian Gagea is a British Red Data Book plant.

Early spring in the European rocky and grassy steppes begins with the colour yellow, and the predominant species is probably the **Yellow Pheasant's Eye** or **Adonis** (*Adonis vernalis* L.). Its scientific name comes from the ancient god who in Asia Minor was the symbol of the cycle of death and rebirth in nature.

The Yellow Pheasant's Eye is a perennial herb of the Buttercup family (*Ranunculaceae*). It is conspicuous for its light yellow, glossy satin flowers, measuring 5 to 6 cm in diameter, with 12–20 petals. The flowers open in April and May. Like a small sunflower, it shines out in the steppe grass only a few centimetres above the ground and later with a growing herbaceous stem in reaches 20 to 40 cm in height. After flowering, the flower changes into a rounded head of beak-shaped achenes. A characteristic feature of the plant are the bright green leaves which are two to four pinnate into narrow linear leaflets.

The Yellow Pheasant's Eye comes from southeastern Europe. Sometimes it is considered as a typical pontic steppe species. Its north-western border passes through central Europe from Sweden (Gotland) to central France. It is not native in Britain, but very much appreciated by gardening devotees. It grows in tufts on rocky and grassy steppes, but also in forest steppes on the edges of warm oak groves and pine woods. It grows on various grounds, from limestone rocks to deep loess, but mostly in calcareous soil.

Like most species of the Buttercup family, the Yellow Pheasant's Eye is a poisonous herb. Cattle will avoid it on pastures. Its properties encourage the activity of the heart and that is why it is an important medicinal plant. The flowering herb is col-

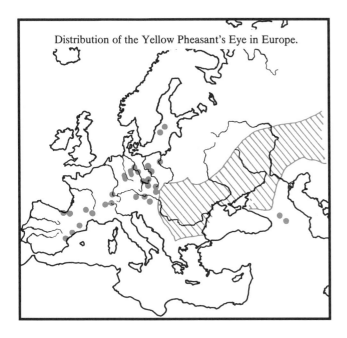

Distribution of the Yellow Pheasant's Eye in Europe.

lected, but in central Europe the Yellow Pheasant's Eye is an officially protected species. The drug made from the plant is imported. It is also a popular decorative plant due to its appearance, cultivated mainly in rock gardens. People sometimes acquire the plant from the wild populations and therefore contribute toward its destruction. However, the Yellow Pheasant's Eye can be bought at horticultural centres for a reasonable price, and what is more, there is almost one hundred percent certainty that these cultivated plants will grow and thrive in the garden. Some of its

habitats were destroyed when grassy steppes were transformed into fields and other cultures. However, on the other hand, a recovery of the plant can be observed on deserted vineyards for instance. In recent years recreation and hiking, with its trampling, camping and the construction of permanent recreational facilities, has also greatly contributed towards the destruction of the biotopes of this protected and rare plant. In Germany, Austria, Poland, Czech and Slovak Republics and Hungary a number of protected areas exist which were set up mainly due to the occurrence of Yellow Pheasant's Eye.

Another European species which requires protection belongs to the Rockrose family (*Cistaceae*) and is called **Hoary Rockrose** (*Helianthemum canum* (L.) Baumg.). It is a perennial growing 10 to 20 cm high, creating a more or less compact sub-shrub. The herbaceous stems bear opposite tiny, 1 to 3 cm long leaves which are greyish-green on the front and thickly tomentose beneath. The 5-part flowers in loose racemes measuring about 1 cm in diameter, are a clear yellow colour. During flowering — from May to July — the flowers are very numerous and the plant is conspicuous and decorative.

The Hoary Rockrose is mainly widespread on rock habitats throughout Europe. It grows on limestone and dolomitic rocks, sun-lit and shaded rocky hillsides. With its strong, long taproot it penetrates very deeply (up to about 1 m) into rock fissures.

It is a relatively rare species of hilly limestone regions in central parts of Germany (mainly Thuringia and Franconia), in the Alpine foothills and in the lower Carpathian mountain ranges. It is found in abundance in the Protected Landscape Area Český kras (Bohemian karst) between Prague and Beroun. Everywhere in these regions, protected areas have been established which also conserve the Hoary

Distribution of Cheddar Pink in Europe

Rockrose and its community. In Germany the Hoary Rockrose is protected by law. It is an altogether rewarding rock plant but is not much cultivated in gardens.

In Britain the Hoary Rockrose is quite rare. It grows in dry grasslands and on rocky places, often on thin dry turf, generally on limestone, particularly on cliffs. It is very localised in western and north-western England, north Wales, Cumbria, and in the Burren in western Ireland.

The endemic subspecies subsp. *levigatum* M.C.F. Proctor is included in the British Red Data Book. The perennial with hairless, dark green leaves and only 1—3 flowers is confined to one single location in Upper Teesdale, fortunately protected in a National Nature Reserve.

One other rockrose can be found in the British Red Data Book: the **White Rockrose** (*Helianthemum apenninum* (L.) Mill.), which has white flowers with a yellow centre. Flowering at the same time and growing in similar habitats to the Hoary Rockrose, this Mediterranean and west European species occurs in about five locations in Devon and Somerset. Most of these are in protected territories.

The rockroses are mainly found in the Mediterranean. Some lovely species are the Greek and Spanish endemics and these are on the European red list. The Mediterranean is a paradise for the entire Rockrose family (*Cistaceae*). The yellow flowering **Fumana** (*Fumana procumbens* (Dunal) Gren. et Godr.) also grows in abundance in this region. It rarely grows locally in central Europe and was formerly regarded as a species of the Rockrose genus.

The Fumana is a 10 to 20 cm high prostrate subbush with alternate, narrow, linear to needle-like leaves. The solitary pale yellow flowers measure up to 2 cm in diameter. They open up in the sun and close when the sky is overcast, so it is easy to overlook this plant and its charm. The Fumana blooms throughout the summer from June to September. It grows on limestone or at least calcareous rocks, mainly in central and south Europe (absent in Britain), from lowlands to mountain foothills. In Hungary it is also found on the sunny sands of the Great Hungarian Lowlands, for example in the Kiskunság National Park and Biosphere Reserve. It is quite a decorative rock plant.

Rocks are also the native habitat of several very lovely pinks (*Dianthus*) of the Pink family (*Caryophyllaceae*). One of the loveliest is the densely tufted, pinkish-red, scented **Cheddar Pink** (*Dianthus gratianopolitanus* Vill.). The tufts in flower glow red on rocks at the end of May or beginning of June during Whitsuntide. It is often cultivated on rocks and various garden hybrids have also been reared through cultivation. The effort it takes to pull it out of its original habitat usually ends up destroying the plant because its taproot is firmly fixed deep in the rocky fissures. But it is easy to cultivate from a seed.

Cheddar Pink is a perennial greyish-green herb which stands 10 to 30 cm high when in flower. The leaves are linear. The flowers with their bearded and toothed petals, which grow single or in pairs at the end of the stem, measure 2 to 3 cm in diameter.

The Cheddar Pink is a central European species and sometimes is even considered a broader central European endemic. It is also sometimes found further west — on the coastal cliffs of Great Britain. Its English name is derived from its occurrence in the Cheddar Gorge, as Somerset is the only area where it is native. In other parts of England and in Northern Ireland almost ten introductions have been recorded. In central Europe it is found on rocky habi-

tats in warm hills and foothills of mountains (it could also be described as a pre-Alpine species) up to 800 metres above sea level. It grows on calcareous ground (limestone, dolomites) as well as on base rich igneous rocks (basalt, clinkstone, porphyry), quartz to acid rocks (shale, greywacke, conglomerate), also in central European rocky steppes. It grows on sunny and partially shadowed habitats. The eastern border of its scattered range runs through eastern Germany, Poland, the Czech Republic, with a rare occurrence in south Moravia recently described as a new species — the **Moravian Pink** (*Dianthus moravicus* Kovanda) — and Austria.

The Cheddar Pink is included on red lists and red data books in various threat categories in Belgium, the Czech Republic, France, Luxembourg, Germany, Switzerland and also Great Britain. It is protected by law in the Czech Republic, Poland, Aus-

tria, Germany, Switzerland and UK. The Cheddar Pink is also included in the List of rare, endangered and endemic plants of Europe.

The Cheddar Pink in the Oder valley also occurs on sunny sandstone hills. However, it should not be confused with another species which is very characteristic of warm and sunny sands. This is the **Sand Pink** (*Dianthus arenarius* L.). The Sand Pink resembles the Cheddar Pink but it has white flowers. It grows in great abundance in Poland where it is found particularly on the sandy terraces of large rivers in light pine woods and sparse xerotherm grasslands. The only Czech occurrence of the Sand Pink is in the central Elbe Basin in Bohemia. The plants in an isolated, strictly protected and carefully managed locality today show certain morphological differences. It is most likely an endemic subspecies which has also been distinguished as a distinct species, the **Bohemian Pink** (*Dianthus bohemicus* (Novák) Soják).

The British Red Data Book also mentions the **Deptford Pink** (*Dianthus armeria* L.) local and rare in England, Wales and south Scotland, suspected of being endangered. This declining plant, extinct in some countries, grows on dry grasslands, on sandy and rocky soils. It is a short, stiffly branched hairy annual to biennial with reddish pink flowers in small flat clusters.

On rocky habitats, especially in rocky steppes in the Carpathian part of central Europe, decorative and protected tufted species are found, in considerable variety, of the so-called large species of **Common Pink** (*Dianthus plumaris* L.). They have large (up to 4 cm in diameter) scented flowers with white and pink deeply toothed petals. The Common Pink is widely cultivated in Britain and is naturalized in places, sometimes as a component of the very interesting flora of urban walls.

A rare species on the European red list is also another attractive rock plant of the Mint family (*Lamiaceae*): the **Austrian Dragonhead** (*Dracocephalum austriacum* L.). Some 15 to 30 cm high stems with pinnate teeth or pinnately divided leaves grow from a multi-head stock of this perennial herb or sub-shrub and flowers issue from the axil of the leaves at the end of the stems. The large, about 3 to 4 cm long 2-lipped flowers are dark bluish-violet, and more rarely pink or white. The Austrian Dragonhead is a popular and rewarding rock garden flower.

This south European species of a pre-Alpine character extends its range to the north in Austria and the Czech and Slovak Republics. It grows on sunny limestone rocks in rocky steppes, often as single specimens in extremely rocky habitats. It is rarely found in Hungary where, just as in the Czech and Slovak Republics, it is protected by law. Apart from the countries already mentioned, it is also found on red lists in France (also protected as a species), in Italy, Romania and Switzerland (also a protected species). It is on the European red list and on the list of plant species protected according to the Bern Convention.

The bluish-violet flowering **Northern Dragonhead** (*Dracocephalum ruyschiana* L.) also appears on European red lists and official decrees. It is a continental Eurasian species of a pre-Alpine and pre-Altai character. It has already become extinct in Germany, and is rarely found and protected by law in Switzerland, Austria and Hungary. This species is more demanding on the moisture of its habitat than the Austrian Dragonhead.

In Britain, both dragonheads are only occasionally cultivated in gardens, but no further spreading has been recorded yet.

In the introduction to this chapter, we mentioned that some plants of European rocky steppes and similar biotopes are adapted to the extreme conditions (particularly drought) with the fleshy, succulent structure of their bodies, stems and leaves. They collect water in their webs, limit evaporation but pay the price of slow growth. The critical periods of their life are the summer droughts and winter frosts because they are not normally covered with snow in their habitats. The members, in particular, of two genera of the Stonecrop family (*Crassulaceae*) belong to these plants: the Stonecrop (*Sedum*) and the Houseleek (*Sempervivum*). While stonecrops are relatively common, there are several species among houseleeks which deserve greater attention and conservation.

The **Hen and Chickens Houseleek** (*Jovibarba sobolifera* (Sims.) Opiz) has densely crowded, globular, closed rosettes of succulent tough leaves with the tip rolled inwards. The leaves are a bright green, reddish on the tops, and during drought and frost they turn a red to brown colour. From the short axil shoots grow many new rosettes by which the plant propagates vegetatively. In this way entire 'nests' of rosettes appear. We rarely catch this plant in flower. A 10 to 25 cm high, thickly leafed, glandular scarlet stem carrying a flat cluster of flowers grows from old rosettes (which die after flowering). The 6-part to 8-part greenish-yellow flowers measure about 2.5 cm in diameter. The plant flowers from June to September.

The Hen and Chickens Houseleek occurs in Europe's temperate zone. The western border of its range runs through Germany. It is included on the red list of threatened species in Germany and is also protected by law. It is a part of central European rock steppes and their pioneer stages, a characteristic species of the class of *Sedo-Scleranthetea* plant asso-

◁ ◁ The Austrian Dragonhead (*Dracocephalum austriacum*) is a rare European species of rocky habitats. It has large, conspicuous flowers on woolly, sparsely branched stems.

◁ The Hen and Chickens Houseleek (*Jovibarba sobolifera*) is conspicuous for its colonies of closed, orbicular, large and small rosettes of fleshy leaves: it grows on rocks but sometimes also on sands in open pine woods.

The Fennel Moon Carrot (*Seseli hippomarathrum*) is ▽ characterised by its pinnate leaves with dense linear segments and by its very dense umbel of whitish flowers with numerous bracts grown into a collar.

Distribution of the Hen and Chicken Houseleek in Europe.

ciations with a dominant representation of succulent plants. It grows on sunny sites, rooting in shallow humous fine soil either on rocky ledges, edges and flat areas, or penetrates with its roots into crevices. It inhabits both calcareous (limestone, dolomite) and quartz and acid (shale, silicium schist etc.) grounds. In the northern lowlands of eastern Germany, Poland and Russia where there are no rock outcrops, the Hen and Chickens Houseleek occurs in light and sparse pine woods with an open herbal undergrowth on sandy substrata. Gardeners often collect it because it is a rock garden plant. The *Jovibarba* differs from the *Supervivum* genus to which it formerly belonged, with its yellow flowers and six or, sometimes, more petals. The true houseleek flower is red or, less frequently, white. During flowering they have 10 to 20 petals.

On the rocky steppes in Alpine valleys (up to 1,860 m above sea level) grows the very ornamental, often cultivated **Cobweb Houseleek** (*Sempervivum*

arachnoideum L.). Its small leafy rosettes are greyish-green, stuck together with white hairs resembling a cobweb. The plant blooms a lot throughout the summer with large pinkish-red flowers on very short (5–12 cm) stems. It is protected by law in Germany and, like all species of houseleek, in Austria.

Characteristic plants of the rocky steppes in Europe are some species of the Moon Carrots (*Seseli* genus). They belong to the Carrot family (*Apiaceae*) and to a layperson they look like dill. The **Fennel Moon Carrot** (*Seseli hippomarathrum* Jacq.) appears on several red lists of central European countries in various threat categories (endangered in Germany). It is a perennial, bald, entirely greyish-green herb with mostly basal leaves and finely pinnate into linear leaflets. The rounded 10 to 50 cm high stem carries umbels only about 3–4 cm in diameter and compound with very dense white or pale pink umbellets. The Fennel Moon Carrot flowers from June to August. This sub-continental European species has the western border of its range in central Europe which runs through the Rhineland and Thuringia. It is absent from Britain.

The picture of the steppe is a white picture of a rippling sea of flowering feather-grasses. This is the way it is depicted in numerous Russian poems, folk and popular songs. Feather-grasses can also be found on rocky steppes and in central European grasslands which are similar to steppes. They are represented here by at least ten different species. In countries where they occur, they are usually protected, and if they create smaller compact grasslands then they have become a motive for special area protection. We can still see such feather-grass steppes for example in nature reserves in Bohemia, in south Moravia, in the Burgenland in Austria and in many places in Hungary.

The **Ivan's Feather-Grass** (*Stipa joannis* Čelak.) is one of the most widespread of the species. It is a tufted perennial grass with 30 a 80 cm long stems and with narrow basal leaves ending in a brush of hairs. The awn of the lemma is covered with thick, about 0.5 cm long white hairs and when in flower it can be up to 35 cm in length. People have always noticed this conspicuous grass. They had various folk names for it (in Bohemia 'St. Ivan's Beard') and collected it for fresh and dry bouquets. In one conservationist magazine at the beginning of the century, Prague nature conservationists complained about Prague Joes (lads) going on festive excursion by steam-boat to Chuchle where they picked rare flowering feather-grasses and then tickled their lasses with them.

The Ivan's Feather-Grass grows only on rocky and grassy steppes. It is a characteristic plant of the union of the *Festucion valesicae* associations. It is a Mediterranean continental species with the western border of its range in central Europe. This, of course, applies to central European feather-grasses in general. On the western border of their range, feather-grasses are found on islands, islets and individual 'outposts'. The **Sand Feather-Grass** (*Stipa borysthenica* Klokov ex Prokudin in Wulf) grows on warm sands in the Pannonian lowland. The **Bavarian Feather-Grass** (*Stipa bavarica* Martinovský et Scholz) is an endemic of the Frankonian Jura mountains. The **Thin-Leaved Feather-Grass** (*Stipa steno-*

phylla Czern) grows on rocky habitats and in black soil. The **Hairy Feather-Grass** (*Stipa dasyphylla* (Czern.) Trautv.) is a distinct species of the fescue-grass areas of rocky and turf steppes. The most abundant of the central European feather-grasses is *Stipa capillata* L., which is the only one that does not have a hairy awn. Its conservation in central Europe is not a high priority at the present time.

Feather-grasses are not native in Britain. The Ivan's Feather-grass was once supposed to have been found in Cumbria, but evidently this must have been some mistake.

Some species of the interesting **Viper's Grasses** (*Scorzonera* genus) contain remarkable substances, e.g. milk in the roots, rich in content of india-rubber. The Black Salsify (*Scorzonera hispanica* L.) was formerly frequently cultivated as a root vegetable. It was also popular as a medicinal plant with various effects, among others as medicine against snake bites. It is also found in central Europe, growing wild in the open countryside, although not directly in the biotopes we are dealing with in this chapter.

The **Purple Viper's Grass** (*Scorzonera purpurea* L.) is a perennial, 20 to 40 cm high herb with an erect, leafy, bald or slightly hairy stem. The flower heads are composed mainly of outer florets which are a delicate dark red to reddish violet colour. It flowers from May to June. This European/western Siberian species has the western border of its range in central Europe. It occurs in warm areas among steppe grasses, sometimes also in sparse pine woods, on sunlit sites on mainly calcareous soils. The flowers only open up in the early hours. In Germany it grows in islands in limestone and loess hilly country of the central Rhineland and Franconia. It is protected by law there and is included in the red list in the highest threat category.

The Feather-grass (*Stipa joannis*), a true steppe grass, can also be found on central European rocky steppes; however there are also several other, similar and more rare species. Its long feathery awns enable the wind to spread its seeds.

◁ The Purple Viper's Grass (*Scorzonera purpurea*) exposes its light bluish pink flower heads to the sun only in the early morning. The western border of its range runs through central Europe.

The Austrian Viper's Grass (*Scorzonera austriaca*) is ▽ a low rocky steppe plant with a flower head which slightly resembles the dandelion: its stems bear solitary flower heads and lanceolate leaves from a basal rosette.

The Wormwood Sand-Broomrape (*Orobanche arena-* ▷ *ria*) is a strangely beautiful plant without green colouring matter; in the picture it is shown growing among the Field Wormwood (*Artemisia campestris*) on which it is a parasite.

A beautiful ornament of rocky steppes, found mainly on limestone ground, is the low (5—25 cm) light yellow **Austrian Viper's Grass** (*Scorzonera austriaca* Willd.). In western Germany, where it has the western border of its range, it occurs in the upper Rhineland, at Lake Constance and in Bavaria (on the red list it is marked as 'potentially endangered').

An interesting family of vascular plants are the **Broomrapes** (*Orobanchaceae*). In Europe about 30 wild species occur and these mostly grow in grassy communities of a more or less steppe character. This species has a raceme of conspicuous, often very beautifully coloured flowers with long, tubular 2-lipped corollas, but there are no visible leaves be-

longing to this inflorescence, because they are only scaly, not green like the entire stem. In fact Broomrapes are parasites which live off the roots of other green plants. Some species may cause damage to cultivated crops. So, as parasites, the Broomrapes have long remained outside the interest of nature conservation.

Only a total inventory of European flora introduced the broomrapes to European red lists, where they are placed in high threat categories. Of the central European 'steppe' species, the most endangered in the European red list is the **Wormwood Broomrape** (*Orobanche caesia* Reichenb.) with its bluish tinged stems and violet flowers. It acts as a parasite on species of wormwood and only occurs in central Europe in Austria, the Czech and Slovak Republics and Hungary.

The **Wormwood Sand-Broomrape** (*Orobanche arenaria* Borkh.) is more widespread. This is an annual, 20 to 50 cm high herb. The thick scaly, yellow to violet stem ends in a raceme of 15 to 30 bluish-violet flowers which bloom at the beginning of the summer — from June to July. The thermophile *Orobanche arenaria* is found relatively rarely in steppe communities of xerotherm areas where it lives off the Field Wormwood (*Artemisia campestris*). It is on the German red list as an endangered species.

There are five broomrapes listed in the British Red Data Book. The pale yellow **Bedstraw Broomrape** (*Orobanche caryophyllacea* Sm.) has only recently been discovered in two locations in Kent growing as a parasite on Hedge Bedstraw (*Gallium mollugo*). The **Yarrow Broomrape** (*Orobanche purpurea* Jacq.) with bluish-violet flowers is a parasite on Yarrow (*Achillea millefolium*). Formerly more widespread it is now found only in Dorset, the Isle of Wight, Norfolk and Lincolnshire. The robust

Thistle Broomrape (*Orobanche reticulata* Wallr.) is a rapidly declining species now known to exist only in four locations in Yorkshire. Only two areas of occurrence exist (in Somerset and Kent) of the formerly more widespread **Ox-tongue Broomrape** (*Orobanche loricata* Reichenb.) with pale yellow flowers tinged and veined with violet, growing in rocky habitats and grasslands. The last of the five British 'red' broomrapes is the **Carrot Broomrape** (*Orobanche maritime* Pubsl.), with purplish stems occurring very rarely on rough maritime pastures.

On the Pea family (*Leguminosae*), the milk-vetches are the most typical in steppe biotopes. The **Woolly Milk-vetch** (*Oxytropis pilosa* (L.)DC.) is typical of them. The strong, erect stems of this perennial herb are silky and hairy, 10 to 30 cm high and carry 5 to 10 cm long pinnate leaves with 10 to 12 pairs of narrow leaflets and an end leaflet. Pale yellow flowers grow in the axil of the leaves. The plant flowers in June and July. The fruits are small, swollen pods.

The Woolly Milk-vetch is widespread in various steppes in the southern European part of Russia and the Ukraine (even in the Crimean mountains). The western border of its range passes through Germany and France, where it grows in warm and dry (xerotherm) areas in rocky steppes and in dry and open steppe grasslands together with fescues, feather-grasses and other xerophytic grasses. It occurs in rich base, mainly calcareous soils. It is protected by law in western Germany (endangered on the red list) where it grows quite rarely.

Surprisingly, the Woolly Milk-vetch reaches southern Scandinavia at the border of its geographic distribution, but it does not occur in Britain. It may be cultivated locally in rock gardens, but it has not been recorded as having spread to the wild.

Most of Europe's flaxes (*Linum*) of the Flax family (*Linaceae*) appear in biotopes of a steppe character. Some with their blue flowers resemble the now not so extensively cultivated Common Flax. The **Austrian Flax** (*Linum austriacum* L.) is, for example, in Germany and the Czech Republic spontaneously spreading to new locations and has even acquired the reputation of some sort of steppe 'weed'. It also occurs as a naturalized species in Denmark. The **Perennial Flax** (*Linum perenne* L.) is also cultivated as a decorative garden plant. This hairless perennial with dark blue flowers is found rarely in Britain from Essex to Cumbria in a sky blue variety, subsp. *anglicum* (Miller) Oncendon. It is mentioned, but not included in the British Red Data Book. The large-flowered **Hairy Flax** (*Linum hirsutum* L.) is only found in the Pannonian region and its headlands. A member of the German flora is the blue, prostrate, only 5 to 15 cm high *Linum leonii* F. W. Schultz which is a western European to sub-Atlantic species. On the foothills of the Alps (up to about 1,800 m above sea level) in grasslands grows the less distinct steppe type of pinkish-violet **Sticky Flax** (*Linum viscosum* L.). The calcicolous **Thin-leaved flax** (*Linum tenuifolium* L.) with its pale violet flowers grows in rocky steppes and steppe meadows. All these species deserve attention from the point of view of nature conservation. They are found in various categories on European red lists. The *Linum leonii* is even on the European red list.

Especially attractive are yellow flowering species of flax growing mainly in south-eastern Europe. The **Yellow Flax** (*Linum flavum* L.) is a hairless, perennial herb, 20 to 50 cm high. The flower-bearing stems end in a corymb of 5-part golden-yellow flowers with a diameter of 2.5 to 4 cm. Like the other species of

◁ ◁ The Woolly Milk-vetch (*Oxytropis pilosa*) has dense whitish yellow flowers in racemes growing from axils of odd-pinnated leaves.

◁ The Yellow Flax (*Linum flavum*), a handsome glabrous herb with narrow, angular stems densely covered with opposite lanceolate leaves, is an indicator of strongly calcareous ground.

The Thuringian Potentilla (*Potentilla thuringiaca*) has ▽ digitate leaves usually with 7 leaflets in basal rosettes. Its flowers are small and bright yellow. It demands soil which is rich in nutrients but non-calcareous.

The Cornflower *Centaurea triumfetti* is one of the ▷ loveliest European members of the family: the plant is covered with greyish hairs.

steppe flax, the Yellow Flax flowers at the beginning of summer — from June to July.

The western border of its range, or more precisely the last scattered islands of the Yellow Flax, penetrate into Swabia and the Franconian Jura in Germany and the Alpine foothills (it is on the German red list as an endangered species). In central Bohemia it occurs in calcareous rocky steppes and dry grasslands, and is listed as threatened there. Generally, it occurs in dry but fresh grasslands, of a steppe character, in scrubs and on the edge of forests, always on calcareous ground. It is a decorative flower, sometimes cultivated in gardens, particularly in rockeries.

The very low yellow-flowering **Dolomitic Flax** (*Linum dolomiticum* Borb.) is on the European red

list. It is an important Hungarian relict and is endemic there.

The **Thuringian Potentilla** (*Potentilla thuringiaca* Bernh.) represents in our 'steppe' selection a large group of the Rose family (*Rosaceae*). Like most cinquefoils it has 5-part golden yellow flowers. It is an inconspicuous perennial herb with thin stems which are procumbent at the base, 10 to 30 cm high. It flowers from spring to summer — from May to July. It is the rarest of all the cinquefoil species in Europe.

In Thuringia the Thuringian Potentilla evidently grows in such abundance that it has not been included in the eastern German red list. But in western Germany, where it grows as a rarity in the Jura and on gypsum ground at the central part of the Main valley, it is classified as an endangered species, the most endangered of all western German species of cinquefoils. It grows on dry hillsides, in light forests, on the periphery of forests and in pastures. It is a European/western Siberian species. Thuringia, after which it is named, lies on the very edge of its range.

The Thuringian Potentilla occurs as a naturalized species in several places in Scandinavia, but not in Britain. The cinquefoils, however, are represented in the British Red Data Book by two species. The **Rock Cinquefoil** (*Potentilla rupestris* L.) is a medium sized hairy perennial with white flowers, which either grow individually or in lax clusters. The north western border of the range of this European species growing in rocky habitats, slopes and ledges and in open woodland, runs through Britain, Norway and Sweden. Very rare, confined to isolated locations in Wales and Scotland, it is threatened by quarrying and heavy collecting by gardeners and botanists. The second British 'red' species is the **Shrubby Cinquefoil** (*Potentilla fruticosa* L.), an abundantly branched deciduous shrub with yellow flowers, grown in gar-

dens in many forms as an ornamental woody plant. About 17 populations are known to exist on damp rocky ground in Yorkshire, Durham and Cumbria; it also occurs in Ireland.

The Mediterranean is the centre of geographical distribution of dozens of species of the large genus of the Cornflowers and Knapweeds (*Centaurea*) of the Daisy family (*Asteraceae*). There are a number of significant endemics among them. Some 97 species of *Centaurea* are found on the List of rare, endangered and endemic plants of Europe. They occur in the Balkans, on the Iberian Peninsula and on Mediterranean islands, mostly in dry, sunny, rocky or stony habitats. Several of these xerophilous and thermophilous species also extend further north in Europe and are a component of the rocky steppes and similar xerotherm communities there. The most beautiful of these is perhaps the *Centaurea triumfettii* All.

It is a perennial herb, which usually grows to 20 to 30 cm, however sometimes also to about 0.5 m high. The entire plant with its simple or only sparsely branched stems and soft, undivided and entire leaves is usually grey tomentose from the thick hairs. At the ends of the branches, there are mostly large separate decorative flower heads with blue to dark violet, or occasionally pink or white florets. It flowers from June onwards throughout the summer.

The *Centaurea triumfettii* is a lovely and rewarding rock plant. In the wild it does not escape the attention of people and they either pick it or dig it up for their gardens even though it is not likely that the plant will grow on the new site. However, more damage is being caused by the destruction of its habitats.

The British Red Data Book includes the **Star-thistle** (*Centaurea calcitrapa* L.). This is a short to tall abundantly branched perennial with pinnately

lobed leaves and pale purple flower heads of up to 1 cm in diameter. Although very often introduced as an impurity in lucerne and clover seed for agricultural use, this central and southern European species is believed to be native in several locations in sandy or chalky soils along the Sussex coast.

In warm, sunny and dry habitats grows the **Honeywort** (*Trinia glauca* (L.) Dumort.) of the Carrot family in stony and sandy soils. It is a perennial, not very conspicuous herb, 10 to 40 cm high, with 2—3 pinnate leaves with slender division. It is totally hairless and a greyish-green colour. The tiny yellowish or greenish flowers bloom from April to June.

The Honeywort penetrates central and western Europe from the southern Mediterranean. It grows on chalky, but sometimes also on neutral to acid grounds, on rocky steppes, on open dry grassland over limestone and on sandy banks. It is remarkable because it belongs to a very rare group of plants in central Europe which have earned the title 'steppe runners' from botanists. In the period of the ripening of the seeds, the entire overground part of the herb often falls away, the wind carries it across the forest-free steppe and it sows its seeds in this way.

The most northern headlands of *Trinia glauca's* range in central Europe are some warm regions of the central Rhineland, central Pomerania and the Jura, as well as rocky and grassy sunny hillsides of southern Moravia. It is listed as endangered in Germany and threatened in the Czech Republic.

But the geographical distribution of the Honeywort (or Honewort, as it sometimes is called) extends as far as Britain, where it is confined to southern Devon, northern Somerset and Gloucestershire. Presently it occurs there in some 10 locations in dry limestone grasslands. Protected from habitat destruction in two Nature Reserves and five Sites of

◁ ◁ The Honeywort (*Trinia glauca*) has reddish, grooved, rather tortuous stems: this herb is rounded in shape and has numerous umbels of small thick umbellets of very small, yellowish or greenish flowers.

◁ The Fastigiate Gypsophila (*Gypsophila fastigiata*) has linear, rather fleshy leaves, small flowers in dense inflorescence forming clusters at the tops.

The Spiked Speedwell (*Veronica spicata*) has tufted ▷ stems with sparse opposite lanceolate leaves, and at their tops a narrow inflorescence resembling a spike: the species is quite variable with a number of subspecies and varieties. It grows on dry glasslands, rocks, on both acid and calcareous rocks which can be both rich and poor in nutrients, and in sandy soils.

The Sand Yellow Cudweed (*Helichrysum arena-* ▷ *rium*) belongs to the Cudweeds. The erect, white woolly ▽ stems bear clusters of dry papery flower heads of a lemon yellowish colour some of which later turn orange.

Special Scientific Interest, it has nevertheless — because of its rare occurrence — been included in the British Red Data Book.

The Latin and English names of the *Gypsophila* of the Pink family (*Caryophyllaceae*) indicate the occurrence of the plants on gypsum — rich soil and rocks. This particularly applies to one species, the **Fastigiate Gypsophila** (*Gypsophila fastigiata* L.) which is a typical plant of rocky steppes on steep southern slopes of gypsum hills in the foothills of the Harz mountains, for example in the excellent botanical area of Kyffhäuser in Germany. However, in another subspecies, the Fastigiate Gypsophila also occurs on unstable, moving sands in the warm lowlands of central Europe. The western border of the range of this 'steppe relict' passes through Sweden, Denmark, Germany, Belgium, Holland and France.

The Fastigiate Gypsophila is a perennial, robust herb usually only 15 to 40 cm high. Both sterile, thickly leafed stems and flower-bearing ascendant stems grow from a branched rhizome. The leaves are narrow, linear, sometimes rather fleshy. Flat-topped clusters are composed of many tiny white or pinkish flowers. These flowers bloom from June to August.

In European communities of steppe, or more precisely of a xerotherm character, are several species of the Speedwells (*Veronica*) of the *Scrophulariaceae* family. The most widespread inhabitant of these biotopes is the **Spiked Speedwell** (*Veronica spicata* L.), a species of relatively broad ecological scope, but it is certainly a thermophilous and xerophilous species, and also rather variable, divided into a number of subspecies.

As its common name indicates, this perennial resembles a spike with its very long and narrow racemose inflorescence. The hairs make it a bit greyish green in colour. Its erect stems are 20—40 cm long. The tiny clear blue to dark violet flowers bloom from June to early autumn. It can still be seen in flower in September or even in October.

The Spiked Speedwell is an European/western Siberian species. In central, northern and western Europe it often occurs in warm lowlands and hills, on rocky steppes and sometimes on dry grasslands, in drier meadows and pastures, on bushy hillsides, at the edge of forests and roads, on moving sand dunes or on sandy soils in the undergrowth of light pine woods. In can quite frequently be found in appropriate habitats in the northern lowlands of Germany and Poland. The west German red list registers it an endangered species.

The Spiked Speedwell is a British Red Data Book species and officially protected. Formerly it was more widespread, but now it remains only in the dry grassland of East Anglia. This applies, however,

only to the subspecies *spicata*. The subsp. *hybrida* (hybridised with Long-leaved Speedwell — *Veronica longifolia* L.) is more abundant on limestone rocks in western England and in Wales. In Britain and throughout Europe, the Spiked Speedwell is widely cultivated in gardens.

A wild central European herb belonging to the most popular of flowers is a relative of garden immortelles, the *Helichrysum arenarium* (L.) Moench of the Daisy family (*Compositae*). This 20 to 40 cm high perennial herb has narrow leaves in ground rosettes and leafy white or greyish stems. The round, over 0.5 cm long flower heads on 3 to 20 corymbose panicles at the top of the stems are a lemon to golden yellow colour. They flower from July to the beginning of October. They are very dry and last a long time in shape and colour, and therefore the *Helichrysum arenarium* has also been a favourite for dry or winter bouquets. It was also used as a medicinal plant or even an insect repellent.

The *Helichrysum arenarium* has a large European/western Siberian range. In the west it reaches Belgium and the Netherlands, in the north right up to Scandinavia. It occurs almost exclusively in warm and dry regions on sands and sandy soils. It grows in xerotherm open communities, in dry grasslands, at forest edges, road verges, on banks and in light pine woods. Up until recently, nature conservation did not pay much attention to it because it was regarded as a common plant and almost as a weed. However, in recent years botanists and nature conservationists have discovered that the *Helichrysum arenarium* has disappeared from a number of well-known locations. Today it is among the strongly threatened species on the German and Czech red lists and in Germany in 1980 it became legally protected by a federal decree.

One of the rarest plants of warm central European sand dunes, strictly confined to sand soils, is the **Jurinea** (*Jurinea cyanoides* (L.) Reichenb.). It also belongs to the Daisy family (*Compositae*) and resembles the knapweed. This perennial herb grows to a height of 0.25—0.50 m. The pinnately-lobed basal leaves are hairy, and later bald, with pale, cotton-like undersides. The sparsely leafed stem carries one large (2 to 3 cm in diameter) flower head at the end of the branches. The red-violet flowers bloom from the end of July to September.

The Jurinea is a continental species mainly growing in south-eastern and eastern Europe. The western border of its range passes through central Europe. It runs from Mecklenburg-Vorpommern (but where today it is listed as missing) through Brandenburg to Saxony-Anhalt. Records from Thuringia are most likely mistaken, but the Jurinea grows in central

Pomerania, Franconia and the Rhineland. About two locations survive of the former wider occurrence in the central Elbe basin in Bohemia. The species is now on the European red list.

The Jurinea roots up to 2 m in depth. It grows on open, unstable sands, preferably chalky, it is a sand dune plant. It is a characteristic species of the *Jurineo-Koelerietum* plant association of the union of sparse sandy steppes *Koelerion glaucae* with the dominating Grey Koeleria (*Koeleria glauca* (Schkuhr) DC.) grass.

In central Europe one more species of Jurinea is found whose range penetrates the rocky, grassy steppes in the most southern parts of Moravia and Slovakia. This is the extremely rare *Jurinea mollis* (L.) Reichenb.

We end our excursion to the sandy steppes with the **Kochia** (*Kochia laniflora* (S. Gmel.) Borb.). It belongs to the rather unattractive Fat Hen family (*Chenopodiaceae*). It is an annual herb, reddish brown in colour, with linear to thread-like leaves. The leafy inflorescence is composed of tiny flowers at large intervals, but grouped at the top of the stem in conspicuous pale hairy balls. It flowers from mid-summer to early autumn, from July to October.

This central European steppe relict of Eurasian continental distribution is also a typical sand plant, a so-called psammophyte. It grows in habitats similar to those of the previous species. It is typical of the community of *Jurinea cynoides* and the *Koeleria glauca*. In Germany it is a species which is in danger of extinction and isolated areas of occurrence are found in the central Rhineland around Mannheim. It occurs throughout Hungary and from here it penetrates several localities in the Czech and Slovak Republics and the Austrian March and Danubian basins, and on sand banks in Kráľovsky Chlmec, south-eastern Slovakia.

DRY MEADOWS, PASTURES, HILL GRASSLANDS

The Large Pasque Flower (*Pulsatilla grandis*) has large, pale bluish violet flowers up to 5 cm long; it differs in its location from the similar western European Common Pasque Flower (*Pulsatilla vulgaris*).

In this chapter we move to another part of the European countryside — the dry grasslands. These are grasslands of various types and origin, but they do have one thing in common. They did not evolve naturally but as a result of human activity in terms of the replacement of former forest land. Human activity is also required if these areas are to remain forest free, because, as already stated, in most of Europe, vegetation without man's intervention gradually turns into woodland. On pastures which have not been mown or used for grazing, the grass grows tall, seeds of woody plants germinate, bushes appear and then finally the forest. In more remote areas — for example in foothills and mountains, which people have abandoned in favour of towns — all the small meadows and pastures have been overgrown by forest.

The grassland plant formations are of great ecological importance. Turf is a perennial community which protects soil against erosion. Semi-natural grasslands are of even greater importance for the preservation of plant wealth with valuable properties. The semi-natural plant communities originally appeared as a result of human activity, but man went on to restrict their growth by ploughing, for instance, as well as excessive use of manure fertilizers and toxic chemicals (pesticides, etc.).

In this chapter we have selected plants from the communities of meadow steppes which are still thermophilous and xerophytic, but to a far lesser extent than the biotopes of the previous chapter. We are talking about the so-called mesophylous grasslands (i.e. with moderate demands with regard to moisture, nutrients, soil reaction and oxygen), and this is also reflected in the name of the union of plant associations which experts call *Mesobromion erecti*. This union belongs to the *Brometalia erecti* order and the grass name can be discerned in the name of the predominant species in these communities — the Upright Brome (*Bromus erectus* Huds). The Upright Brome is an erect, robust tufted grass growing to about 0.5 m in height with a compact, narrow panicle. However, there are communities in which the Upright Brome does not occur. A leading species of different plant associations, sometimes delimited to separate unions or subunions is Tor-grass (*Brachypodium pinnatum* (L.) P. Beauv.) which at first glance resembles the Upright Brome. It is also called the Heath False-brome.

However, what interests admirers of rare and threatened plants is the fact that a large number of flowers are found in these meadow steppes which have become of great interest to nature conservationists in Europe over the past two decades — the orchids. The most beautiful orchids in these communities grow and then disappear because semi-natural flowering grasslands are not advantageous for the farmer, who constantly increases yields and industrializes the agricultural countryside. And so even if areas of grasslands are so large that these flowers do not disappear completely with the creation of arable land, they tend to be removed or re-seeded, so that the result is a monoculture of two or three grass species which are greatly encouraged by manure and fertilizers. Flowering meadows are on the decline.

Rescue for the plant communities of the 'meadow steppes' appears to be coming in the shape of protected territories. However, as with the biotopes of the previous chapter, the dry grasslands also require constant care, i.e. mowing and grazing or some simulation of this activity. Sometimes rapid scorching by fire (along the surface) is used, under careful supervision of course and on a serious scientific basis. Dry meadows with orchids at the Upper Bavarian Ammersee Lake are being overgrown by woody plants and will lose their floral beauty if they are not mowed or grazed in conjunction with special territorial protection. One of the outposts of colourful flora with many 'steppe' features are two hills on moraines not far from the lower reaches of the Oder river in eastern Germany — the protected natural territory of Geesower Hügel. One of the rarest species of grasslands with the Tor-grass in central Europe is the very rare Toothed Orchid (*Orchis tridentata* Scop). An interesting phenomenon occurred some years ago at the Geesower Hügel reserve. In view of the fact that territorial protection was declared here, meadows stopped being mown and grazed and the population of rare orchids moved several dozen metres away lower down the slope to the fallow land of an abandoned field.

However, the conservation of flowering meadows should not be restricted to sanctuaries in reserves. Unless farmers themselves comprehend the importance of the flower oases in the countryside for their healthy ecological regime, their diversity and beauty, then there cannot even be any talk of conservation and creation of a favourable environment. The English have an interesting way of solving this problem. On recultivated sites of activity (e.g. mining) which have affected the natural balance and even in housing estates and industrial areas, they are establishing attractive grasslands where threatened plants can also be included.

Some of the most attractive flowers of dry grass-

▽ Mowed or extensively grazed flower meadows are unfortunately disappearing from the European countryside: these meadows once supported a wealth of flora, including terrestrial orchids.

In reserves all over Europe dry grasslands have been ▷ preserved which are habitats of rare plant species. Pictured here is a reserve of the Eastern Pasque Flower (*Pulsatilla patens*), a species on the European red list, in northern Bohemia, Czech Republic.

The Common Pasque Flower (*Pulsatilla vulgaris*) ▷▽ flowering in April in the protected site Devil's Dike (England). Cf. p. 88.

lands, sometimes also growing on rocky steppes, are the lowland and hilly species of the European **Pasque Flower** (*Pulsatilla*) of the Buttercup family (*Ranunculaceae*). Its scientific name is interesting: it relates to the fact that the Pulsatilla has large individual campanulate flowers (Latin: *pulsare* = to move, to ring), and is appropriately expressed by its German names Küchenschelle, Kuhglocke (cow bell). The English name refers to Easter time, as the plant flowers in the spring.

The **Eastern Pasque Flower** (*Pulsatilla patens* (L.) Mill.) is on the European red list as well as on the Annex of the Berne Convention. Its 3—4 cm long bluish-violet flowers are at first (or during bad weather) campanulate, later (in the sunlight) they open up and spread widely. The hairy, erect stems are 10 to 15 cm, when in fruit 30—40 cm high (the decorative, silvery achenes are up to 5 cm long). The

most reliable identification mark are the trifoliate basal leaves which, however, only develop after flowering. The plant flowers from the end of April to the beginning of May.

The Eastern Pasque Flower is a European species. It is most widespread in Poland and in the more northern temperate zone of the former USSR. It is scattered in its distribution in the north-west up to Finland and Sweden, and in the south-west to the Czech Republic and to Germany (Bavaria), where it is protected by law and found on red lists in the highest threat categories. Formerly, it also grew in the eastern part of Germany, but recently its occurrence there has not been reconfirmed. Of the several locations on the eastern border of Hungary only one population of 150 to 160 individual plants has survived, so the species is listed there as being critically endangered and is strictly protected.

The slightly thermophilous Eastern Pasque Flower (found in regions with a warm summer) grows in lowlands and hilly country on drier, nutrient rich and acid sandy, stony to rocky (particularly in the Czech and Slovak Republics) ground. It is most likely to be found in drier grassland communities of the central European steppe to rocky steppe type and in light pine woods in the east of Europe.

It is a very decorative plant. Many rock gardeners try to acquire live plants growing in the open countryside and thereby endanger and weaken the surviving population. The Pasque Flower can be cultivated from seeds, but it is not easy because there tend to be problems with germination (the precise time of the maturity of the seeds has to be known and sowing must take place immediately). The Hungarian Botanical Institute Vácrátöt cultivated seedlings to strengthen the decimated population in the open countryside. As can be seen, it is the destruction of its habitat which presents the greatest danger to this rare plant.

However, even in the protected areas, the Eastern Pasque Flower requires special care. The herb and grass growths which, under traditional cultivation methods of semicultural grasslands, were removed by mowing and grazing, are suppressing the plant. It also appears that it is being damaged by insecticides, herbicides and fertilizers blown in by the wind or carried by water drained from local, intensively farmed land.

Pasque Flowers are poisonous plants. They contain some interesting substances, particularly anemonine and protoanemonine. Formerly they were picked and used as curative herbs. This applies to the **Common Pasque Flower** (*Pulsatilla vulgaris* Mill). This species differs from the Eastern Pasque Flower above all in its bipinnate to tripinnate leaves. It is quite widespread in the western part of central Europe, particularly in Germany, but can also be found in Scandinavia, and Great Britain, where it is generally declining. It grows locally in the Cotswolds, the Chilterns and East Anglia, many areas of occurrence being protected in nature reserves and Sites of Special Scientific Interest. In the Alpine valleys of Switzerland it grows up to 2,000 m above sea level. In the eastern part of central Europe grows the **Large-flowered Pasque Flower** (*Pulsatilla grandis* Wender.), also regarded as a subspecies of the previous species. The variable **Small Pasque Flower** (*Pulsatilla pratensis* (L.) Mill.) has the centre of its range in central Europe. It has a number of subspecies, varieties and forms of even smaller plants with smaller campanulate drooping flowers varying in colour from pale yellow through to light violet and up to violet black.

The **Bractless Bastard Toadflax** (*Thesium*

ebracteatum Hayne) of the sole European genus of the mainly tropical Sandalwood family (*Santalaceae*) is an example of a rare but very inconspicuous species. It too is on the European red list although a layperson — and sometimes a less observant botanist — can often overlook it. The toadflaxes are semiparasitic annual or perennial herbs, only 15—40 cm high with green stems, narrow alternating leaves and tiny, bell-shaped greeny whitish flowers in racemes or panicles. As the name indicates, the important distinguishspecies there are three. It is actually the bracteoles which are missing.

The Bractless Toadflax is a European continental species which is scattered over a wide area and rarely grows in central Europe. It is in the highest threat category on the red list of eastern Germany (only in Brandenburg, extinct in Saxony, missing in Saxony-Anhalt and Mecklenburg), the Czech Republic (only one station), Austria, Denmark and Romania. It may still survive in Lower Saxony and Schleswig-Holstein (also in the highest threat category), although, according to some sources, it has already gone missing there or is extinct.

The inconspicuous, very slender Bractless Toadflax grows mainly in meadows with acid and sandy (northern parts of Germany, Poland) or boggy (the Czech Elbe basin) soils. It is also found in warmer light pine woods, but it appears that its ecology has not yet been sufficiently examined. It is a good example of a species whose conservation depends on effective management in protected biotopes.

The **Spring Gentian** (*Gentiana verna* L.) of the Gentian family (*Gentianaceae*) is found in Europe not only in the mountains, but also in lowlands and hilly country. We have included it in this chapter because it grows on rather dry meadows — both lowland and highland. It is a handsome perennial with a basal leaf rosette and a simple, single-flowering erect stem about 5 cm long. The flower blooms — according to the location of the habitat — from March to June and is renowned for its unique dark azure blue colour. The Spring Gentian is the dream of all rock gardeners. Various varieties have been cultivated which can be purchased at garden centres, so the destruction of the natural habitats has become unnecessary.

Like almost all other species of gentians, the Spring Gentian is protected by law throughout Europe. So far it is still quite common on mountain meadows, on dry to fresh, calcareous soils up to the altitude of over 2,500 m above sea level. It is distributed across Eurasia and can be found in the east in Mongolia as well as in the last surviving (and obviously strictly protected) areas of occurrence in the British Isles. The Spring Gentian is a rare plant growing in stony, grassy places on limestone in Yorkshire, Durham and Cumbria. 40 of the 50 or so existing populations are in National Nature Reserves. The species however still suffers, mainly due to over-collecting by gardeners and botanists, although it is a protected species. There are also approximately 30 Spring Gentian locations in western Ireland. The Spring Gentian is included in the British Red Data Book. It is critically endangered in those areas where there are no high mountains, particularly in eastern Germany and the Czech Republic. Once it was found in abundance in the fresh meadows with the Purple Moor-grass or in drier meadows in the union of the Upright Brome, in the Alpine foothills (Alpenvorland), in the northern part of eastern Germany (extinct today), Thuringia (only two stations remain) and in some parts of Bohemia, particularly in the southern and western parts (of the several dozen, or possibly hundreds of original sites, only a few remain, and these are being destroyed). The reason for the decline of this charming flower from the lowland and hilly country meadows is the intensive farming (fertilization, land amelioration, etc.).

The **Cross Gentian** (*Gentiana cruciata* L.) looks different. It is a robust perennial plant, 10 to 50 cm high with thick leaved and multi-flower stem. Its scientific species name is derived from the decussate, tough, almost leathery leaves. The 4-lobed flowers, with the outside of the corolla a greenish blue and the inside a bright blue, are arranged individually or in clusters at the base of the leaves in the upper half of the stems. They bloom from June to September or to the beginning of October.

The Cross Gentian is a species protected throughout Europe and is found on most red lists in the medium to higher threat categories. It has a broad range in Europe and western Siberia reaching the Netherlands in the west. It grows up to an altitude of over 1,000 m above sea level, particularly in the Alpine and Carpathian regions. It is a slightly thermophilous plant, clearly calciphilous and quite demanding with regard to its soil conditions. It is found in most deep, nutrient rich clay soils and loess. It grows in habitats which are exposed to full sunlight and in semi-shade. The most typical biotopes for it are dry, grassy meadows where Tor-grass or Upright Brome is predominant. However, it can also be found in scrub on hillsides, on woodland borders and in light pine woods, particularly at lower mountain altitudes.

Just a few decades ago flora handbooks and atlases stated that the wild European **Green-winged Orchid** (*Orchis morio* L.) was an abundant and common plant everywhere. However, since then this species has become a European rarity. There used to be almost 2,000 sites of the Green-winged Orchid in eastern Germany and today there are only about a dozen. For the Czech and Slovak Republics experts estimate that the total number of sites has decreased by 80% and in some regions the occurrence has decreased to 10% or less of the former state. The species is also decreasing rapidly in Britain. Thus in Shropshire, for example, 32 of the 56 recorded locations are extinct or missing. Elsewhere in Britain the situation is similar or even worse.

◁ The Bug Orchid (*Orchis coriophora*) has flowers in a dense cylindrical inflorescence which are small, most often brownish red and smell rather unpleasant; it is one of the most sensitive species of orchids now becoming extinct in Europe.

▽ The Military Orchid (*Orchis militaris*) has a characteristic helmet in the upper part of the flower composed of perianth segments: the species is distinctly calcicole, but also colonizes secondary habitats.

The Early Purple Orchid (*Orchis mascula*) has a long, ▷ cylindrical, relatively lax inflorescence of pink to purple flowers with a three-lobed lip with deep red spots in the centre and a cylindrical spur. It can be found in mountain meadows at over 2,000 m above sea level.

The Green-winged Orchid of the Orchid family (*Orchidaceae*) is a perennial herb with small underground orbicular tubers. The bluish green lanceolate leaves create a ground rosette and there are several sheathing leaves on the stems. The erect 10 to 30 cm high stem ends in a loose 5 to 12 cm long spike with 7 to 15 (sometimes as many as 25) flowers. The flowers, with a helmet in the shape of a jester's cap (Latin: *morio* = jester), with trilabiate lip and a blunt cylindrical spur, measure over 2 cm. They are mostly various shades of purple (from light pink to darker shades), and more rarely pale or white. They bloom from the end of April to the end of May.

Like many other species or genera of European orchids, the Green-winged Orchid used to be picked as a medicinal plant. The tubers contain a so-called dried tuber mucus which was used for making medicines (it is still used in Asia Minor). It was believed that the orchid could increase male potency and this was reflected in its common name in several languages including German (Knabenkraut = boy's herb).

The Green-winged Orchid is a typical European species. It is found from Spain to the British Isles, southern Scandinavia, Estonia (the northernmost point), Belarus, the Ukraine, Romania, the former Yugoslavia, northern Italy and France. In central Europe, as mentioned, it has become very rare. It grows in dry meadows in grasslands together with the Upright brome, the False oat-grass (*Arrhenatherum elatius*) or the Purple moor-grass. It can grow in dry to calcareous and mildly acidic soils, however it is found most often in neutral, clay and loam soils which are fairly rich in nutrients. It cannot tolerate fertilizers, and the chemicals used in the farming of meadows is one of the main causes of its drastic decline. It can withstand a reasonable amount of graz-

ing and it would even appear that it thrives with extensive sheep grazing.

Another orchid, named after its special smell **Bug Orchid** (*Orchis coriophora* L.), has disappeared from central Europe almost without trace. It belongs to the least conspicuous of the orchids. It is a slim herb only 15 to 30 cm high with brownish red, green veined flowers in a cylindrical inflorescence. It flowers from May to June and sometimes even in July, therefore much later than the Green-winged Orchid.

Although the typical habitats of the Bug Orchid should be damp meadows particularly of a boggy character, this orchid also grows on lime free, neutral or even slightly acidic ground, in damp and dry habitats, in lowlands, on foothills and lower moun-

ain areas (in Europe the uppermost limit of its occurrence is 1,500 m and in North Africa up to 2,150 m above sea level). However, these are warm and relatively sunny habitats. In western Germany it is found in dry grasslands with Upright Brome, in Switzerland in the Valais canton it grows in the bend of the Rhône river, at Martigny even on rocky steppes together with feather-grasses.

The Bug Orchid is the most sensitive of all the orchid species. Its almost total decline on the northwestern border of its range was not only caused by the direct destruction of its habitats, but also by indirect environmental influences. Not even protection in nature reserves (for example in the central Bohemian Elbe basin) could save it from extinction. Its former range was in central and southern Europe (and also in North Africa) extending towards the east through the Balkans right over to Asia Minor, and through the Ukraine and Russia as far as the Caucasus. The Bug Orchid has already become extinct in Belgium, the Netherlands and the Czech Republic. In eastern Germany, where a total of 270 sites were known to have existed, it has gone missing. The survival of this rarity in central Europe is uncertain.

Even among central European orchids there are still plenty of vigorous species which are capable of settling in new, suitable habitats. A relatively robust species is the **Military Orchid** (*Orchis militaris* L.) which grows up to 0.5 m high and is named after the oblong ovate helmet composed of perianth segments. These are light pink, ash grey, violet inside with purple dots. Specimens with white flowers are very rare. The large, light green leafy ground rosette tends to be partly brown at the tips, burned by the night frost when growing too early in the spring. The plant flowers in May and June. In eastern Germany, for example around Berlin, it was recorded that this

orchid spontaneously settled on abandoned clay pits. A secondary occurrence has been recorded of this orchid growing on artificial dikes in Bavaria. Train passengers travelling along the banks of Lake Geneva at the end of spring might notice Military Orchids in flower on cuttings and banks at the side of the railway track between Geneva and Lausanne (but only on calcareous soils).

The Military Orchid is a calciphilous plant and in this respect it can be regarded as a plant indicator. It is also thermophilous. It can be found in dry grasslands — the central European meadow steppes, but a number of sites are also known on almost marshy swamps where the Purple moor-grass predominates, or in the undergrowth of floodplain forests.

The range of the Military Orchid stretches in a broad belt from northern Spain through central Europe to the Urals and continues on to Siberia. Its range also extends northwards to southern Scandinavia, the Baltic states and even includes the compact St. Petersburg area. In England the Military Orchid was formerly probably quite widespread in Hertfordshire, Middlesex, Berkshire, Oxfordshire and Surrey but is now restricted to small numbers of specimens in Buckinghamshire and a large population in Suffolk. The British habitats are mainly beech woods and their borders on chalk. The decline of this species is believed to be caused by changes in the management of its native beech woodland. The existing sites of this protected species are now mostly enclosed: trampling damages the susceptible plant, particularly in the young stage. Some experiments have been carried out to allow access to the public for educational purposes by means of a special nature trail on wooden bridges above the ground.

In the Carpathian region of central Europe the **Early Purple Orchid** (*Orchid mascula* L.) is quite common. It is a variable species with many subspecies, varieties and forms, with light purple, sometimes pink and very rarely white flowers in a long (over 20 cm), sparse, cylindrical inflorescence. It flowers earlier than the previous species, often by the end of April.

The Early Purple Orchid is a European species with Mediterranean and sub-Atlantic tendencies: in the south its range extends to North Africa, in the south-east into Asia Minor and in the north-west right up to the Faeroe Islands and into Scandinavia. It is quite rare today in the lowlands and hilly country of central Europe because the intensive agriculture of land and the forest has destroyed many of its habitats. It grows in nutrient rich and acidic soils in unfertilized meadows, pastures, hillside scrub, sometimes also in open woodlands. In several areas on the Baltic Sea coast, it is an exclusively forest herb. In the central European mountains it climbs pastures and meadows right up to the upper forest border, in the

◁ The Elder-flowered Orchid (*Dactylorhiza sambucina*) ▷ is a small, low orchid with several oblong and colourful leaves; its flowers smell like lilac; they are mostly yellow, but sometimes also purple. It is a declining species.

The Late Spider Orchid (*Ophrys fuciflora*), sometimes ▷ ▷ called 'bumble-bee', has flowers which vary considerably in both shape and colour, but with the lip always resembling a bumble-bee.

Carpathians to about 1,800 m above sea level, and even higher in the Alps. The high mountain specimens are shorter than the lowland and hilly country plants, only 10 to 30 cm high, and have rich reddish violet flowers.

Throughout much of Britain the Early Purple Orchid often grows quite abundantly in localised areas. It is tolerant of light grazing and trampling, but a poor competitor with vigorous grasses.

In European grasslands there also occurs the **Burnt-tip Orchid** (*Orchis ustulata* L.) with its dark brownish coloured flower buds at the top. The Burnt-tip Orchid is mentioned, but actually not included, in the British Red Data Book. A plant of grazed limestone grassland, this species occurs in England as far north as Cumbria, but most frequently in the south and it has become extinct in some places. The **Toothed Orchid** (*Orchis tridentata* Scop.) — in the introduction to this chapter we mentioned its remarkable 'move' in the Geesower Hügel Reserve in eastern Germany — is not native in Britain, the closest occurrence being in southern Germany and eastern France.

The orchid plants have given their name to the entire *Orchidaceae* family. For several decades now special associations have been engaged in the research and conservation of the European representatives of this family. Keen gardeners and nature-lovers have also been attracted to the cultivation of European wild orchids in gardens, which is very difficult if not impossible. Orchids live in very complicated mutual relations with fungi. These fungus elements of their existence, or rather co-existence, are still little known and also greatly damaged by local and general pollution of the environment. It is thanks to the above mentioned specialised associations that it became possible to transfer individual endangered plants to habitats where the basic conditions for the existence of plants have not as yet disappeared, to cultivate wild orchids in culture and strengthen the weak populations in the open countryside.

Species with a relatively dense inflorescence of small flowers and with fingerlike divided tubers were previously also ascribed to the Orchid genus. Now they have been separated as **Marsh Orchids** (*Dactylorhiza* genus).

A beautiful natural jewel in spring (flowers from April) is the short (10 to 20 cm) **Elder-flowered Orchid** (*Dactylorhiza sambucina* (L.) Soo), whose name derives from its sweet-smelling, large flowers. The flowers measure about 2 cm in diameter, being at first in a dense egg-shaped and later in a cylindrically elongated spike. They are usually yellow and less frequently purplish red.

The Elder-flowered Orchid is a European species, but can also be found in isolated occurrence in southern Scandinavia and on the Iberian Peninsula. The species is not native in Britain. It is declining fast because it is very sensitive towards human intervention and grows in places where it has been the victim of substantial intervention in recent years: in dry grasslands in hills, foothills and at lower levels of mountains (in the Alps to 1,200 m, in the Carpathians at almost 1,500 m above sea level). It shows a certain thermophilous tendency, but is not found where it is too dry. It grows in both calcareous and acid soils. It is tolerant to grazing and mowing, so it often exists in open broadleaved woodland and scrub. Although like most orchids throughout Europe, it is protected by law, it is disappearing from the wild rapidly, including nature reserves.

The members of the *Ophrys* genus are undoubtedly some of the most remarkable plants of European flora. They are tiny orchids (most often

10—30 cm, more rarely up to 50 cm high) with relatively large flowers. The genus has about 35 species and the centre of its development and present range is the Mediterranean region. In appearance or shape the *Ophrys* flowers very much resemble species of insect or other arthropods, so people also call the central species of these orchids the 'fly', 'bumblebee', 'bee' or 'spider'. However, this resemblance is not just visual but also has a practical special function. For example the flowers emit the same sort of smell as the females of the relevant species of insects, so they lure the males and these, during their flight from one plant to the next, pollinate the flowers.

The 'fly' in a series of five western and central European *Ophrys* plants is representsed by the **Fly Orchid** (*Ophrys insectifera* L.). The tiny flowers have inconspicuous green outer perianth segments and a broad purple lip with a bluish patch in the middle. In central and north western Europe this is the most widespread species of Ophrys. It grows locally in grasslands of a steppe character, in forest steppes and light pine woods of limestone hills and on mountains (over 1,500 m above sea level). It is found relatively rarely in lowlands and also in damp fens (in the River Peene valley in eastern Germany, in the Great Hungarian Lowland in Hungary). In Britain the Fly Orchid was formerly recorded by botanists as widespread in England; abundant in some of the eastern and south-eastern countries. Now, however, it is regarded as missing or even extinct in some regions. It is scarce in south-western England and Wales, very rare in Ireland, confined more or less to the Burren. It does not occur in Scotland.

Perhaps the finest of the central and north-western European *Ophrys* species is the **Late Spider Orchid** (*Ophrys fuciflora* (Crantz) Moench). It is a perennial herb with relatively strong stems, growing to a height of 15 to 40 cm. The leaves create a more or less typical ground rosette. The sparse inflorescence is composed of 1 to 10 flowers measuring 2 to 3 cm in diameter. The outer perianth segments may be pink, white and greenish and always have greenish veins. The large brownish purple lip has a variable pattern resembling a bumble-bee sitting in the flower. The plant flowers from the end of May to June.

The Late Spider Orchid is widespread in the Mediterranean. In small areas and isolated sites it can be found in central and western Europe where it is carefully monitored and protected. The extreme points of its range are the sunny steppe grasslands in the Benelux countries, in France, southern and central parts of Germany (right up to the central Rhineland), the Moravian and Slovak Carpathians. The beautiful orchid is also at its range border in eastern Kent, where it grows on chalk downs. About eleven areas of occurrence are known; in several of them the species is plentiful, in others limited to a few specimens only. It was probably much more common in the past, but destruction of downland and undergrazing in the last five decades have caused a heavy decline. The Late Spider Orchid is protected in the UK and included in the British Red Data Book. Effective protection for this species lies in protected areas and proper care of its habitats.

Another Mediterranean species with the extreme border of its range in western and central Europe is the **Bee Orchid** (*Ophrys apifera* Huds). The flowers, 3 to 8 in the inflorescence, have relatively long (about 1.5 cm) white to dark red outer perianth segments and a smaller (only about 1 cm long) 3-lobed dark purplish brown lip. This species flowers later

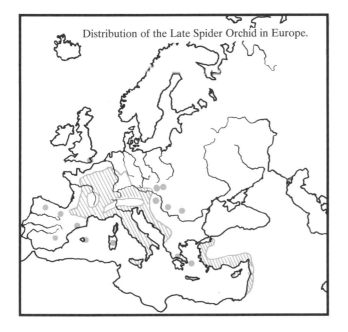

Distribution of the Late Spider Orchid in Europe.

▽ ◁ The Man Orchid (*Aceras anthropophorum*) has a flower lip with four lateral lobes that look like small human figures; unlike the Orchis species, there is no spur in its flower.

▽ The Bee Orchid (*Ophrys apifera*) is conspicuous for its long, reddish outer perianth segments. It flowers later than all other Ophrys species — from June till July.

The Lizard Orchid (*Himantoglossum hircinum*) is a ▷ very robust orchid (up to 1 m high) with numerous flowers in a dense inflorescence from which the over 5 cm long middle lip lobes — 'small ligules' — radiate. The species occurs in western Europe from Germany and Great Britain to North Africa.

The Pyramidal Orchid (*Anacamptis pyramidalis*) can- ▷ ▽ not be confused with any other orchid because of its two distinct features: the pyramidal shape of the dense inflorescence and the small bright purplish red flowers.

than any other Ophrys, not until June and often also in July.

Apart from Poland, the Bee Orchid, although very rare, can also be found in all central European countries. It grows on limestone ground in steppe grasslands, forest steppes and light pine woods. The north-western border of its range extends as far as the British Isles. Erratic in appearance, it occurs locally in most of England, also in the Channel Islands and very rarely in Wales.

The **Early Spider Orchid** (*Ophrys sphegodes* Mill.) is of similar origin, distribution and occurrence. Sometimes it has a very long inflorescence. The flowers have yellowish green to pale yellow outer perianth segments and a brown lip with a clear light pattern in the shape of the letter H. The Early Spider Orchid is a British Red Data Book species, also listed as a legally protected one. Formerly much more widespread in south and south-east England and in the Channel Islands, it is now confined to only 17 locations south of the River Thames in Dorset, Sussex, Kent and in Gloucestershire. One is protected in a National Nature Reserve, one is a National Trust property, six are covered by Sites of Special Scientific Interest. Ploughing-up of old chalk and limestone grassland has had

a detrimental effect on the species populations.

The British Red Data Book also lists the **Berteloni's Bee Orchid** (*Ophrys bertelonii* Mor.). This is an uncommon Mediterranean species with large purplish-black lips with a blue patch. It is, however, not native in Britain. It was only planted in Dorset in one site, but this has not survived.

The similarity of the *Ophrys* flowers to certain small arthropods, particularly insects, is therefore altogether functional. However, some plants have another interesting resemblance. The shape of the lips of certain orchids resembles tiny human figures hanging in the flower. A particularly lovely play by nature is the plant which is popularly called the 'doll' ('Puppe' in German). It is the perennial herb called the **Man Orchid** (*Aceras anthropophorum* (L.) Ait). It grows to a height of over 40 cm and has a divided spike which is up to 20 cm long. The flowers are greenish yellowy brown with purple veins. The lip with its four lateral lobes resembles a manikin sit-

100

Distribution of the Man Orchid in Europe.

ting in the flower. The plant flowers from May to June.

Although the Man Orchid is primarily a southern European orchid with its core range in the western part of the Mediterranean, it is also found in England as far north as Derbyshire. It grows locally in western and central Europe, in warm, sunny grasslands in calcareous, stony, clay soils and loess which are rich in nutrients.

A legend among European orchids is the **Lizard Orchid** (*Himantoglossum hircinum* (L.) Koch) referred to as 'a bear among flowers' by one botanist. It is one of the most robust European orchids. It usually grows to a height of about 0.5 m, but sometimes to nearly 1 m. The dense inflorescence is composed most often of 30 to 50 (more rarely 80) greyish to olive green flowers with purple dots. The flowers are a very unusual shape: the central lobe of the lip, notched at the tip, emerges from a tail-like flower of about 5 cm in length. The specific name 'hircinum' (= goat-like) is derived from the unpleasant smell of this otherwise beautiful plant. The main flowering time of this orchid is in June.

The Lizard Orchid mainly grows in the central and western Mediterranean. From western Europe it has also penetrated into the British Isles. It grows in drier calcareous and humous soils, on sunny hillsides with grassland and scrub and in wood margins and open woodland. In the western part of central Europe it is a local characteristic species of the communities with the Upright Brome. Populations in the most north-eastern range border are almost all protected in reserves on limestone on the foothills of the Thuringia Forest and in the Saale Hills in Germany. During flowering, the plant can easily be found by looking for uprooted vegetation around it, because the Lizard Orchid is a favourite object of interest for na-

ture photographers.

In southern Britain the Lizard Orchid is generally rare, with scattered locations recorded in England as far north as Yorkshire. The populations of this species have fluctuated constantly; the plant was believed to be extinct in about 1900, a rapid expansion was reported between 1920 and 1940, and since 1940 it has been on the decline. The British Red Data Book species, protected by law, is at present missing in the Channel Isles, and thought to survive in only very few permanent colonies. Six of them are protected by Sites of Special Scientific Interest.

Further to the east, in similar habitats the **Adriatic Lizard Orchid** (*Himantoglossum adriaticum* Baumann) with sparse inflorescence and more colourful flowers occurs. It was not distinguished and described until 1978 in the Italian province of Trentino. The **Goat Lizard Orchid** (*Himantoglossum capri-*

101

◁ The Purple Milk-vetch (*Astragalus danicus*) has deep violet flowers within orbicular inflorescence growing on thin stalks at the base of odd-pinnate leaves.

The Autumn Lady's Tresses (*Spiranthes spiralis*) is ▷ a late (flowers from the end of summer to the beginning of autumn), quite tiny and inconspicuous, rare orchid: its inflorescence is unilateral with flowers in a spiral.

The Bulb-Bearing Lily (*Lilium bulbiferum*) has an erect ▷ ▷ densely leafy stem, bearing a single, large, unscented flower of a fiery golden red colour.

The Stemless Milk-vetch (*Astragalus exscapus*) has long ▷ ▽ odd-pinnated leaves with 12 or more pairs of leaflets and a dense cluster of bright yellow flowers in the middle of their rosette.

num M.B. Spreng.) is an eastern Balkan and Black Sea species, also found in Hungary.

The **Pyramidal Orchid** (*Anacamptis pyramidalis* (L.) L.C. Rich.) corresponds to its name. It has relatively small, fleshy red flowers, densely packed in a 3 to 8 cm long pyramidal spike. This 30 to 50 cm high plant flowers from June to July.

It is a Mediterranean-central European species with a certain sub-Atlantic tendency, is clearly thermophilous and calciphilous. It grows in two types of meadow biotopes: in dry grasslands with the Upright Brome and in temporarily damp boggy meadows with the Purple Moor-grass. It is found more frequently in the southern part of central Europe. It is disappearing further north due to changes in farming and other developments in the countryside. In eastern Germany it is classified in the highest threat category in the strictest category of species protection. In Britain the Pyramidal Orchid is still abundant in north to southern Scotland and in the Hebrides. It is one of the most reliable indicators of calcareous soils. In Britain the plant is tolerant of heavy grazing and trampling.

The **Autumn Lady's Tresses** (*Spiranthes spiralis* (L.) Chevallier) is quite a small orchid (20 to 25 cm high) with an interesting biology. It often grows in groups because it reproduces in abundance by subsidiary tubers. The ground leaves create a rosette from which flower-bearing stems grow at the end of summer and in the autumn — in August and September — covered only by tiny compressed scaly leaves. The one-sided, dense, spiral (hence the Latin name of the plant) inflorescence is composed of about 20 tiny white pleasant smelling flowers. Almost the entire herb is glandular on the surface.

The Autumn Lady's Tresses is a European species extending as far as north Africa and Asia Minor. It is also native in Britain (throughout England and Wales and in South Ireland) and even in Iceland. It grows in dry and temporarily damp clay soils which are poor in calcium, in lowlands, hills and lower mountains. It was often found — like many other wild orchids — on sheep pastures. Sheep excrement possibly encourages the development of fungi with which these species live in a symbiosis. The Autumn Lady's Tresses responds well to grazing, trampling, frequent mowing and even to disturbance of the ground. However, most areas of occurrence have disappeared over the last few decades as a consequence of the intensification of agriculture.

A plant which resembles the Autumn Lady's Tresses is the somewhat taller **Summer Lady's Tresses** (*Spiranthes aestivalis* (Poir.) L.C.Rich.) with stems that have leaves on the bottom part. In central Europe it is more rare than the previous species. It grows on meadows which are rather damp, boggy and calcareous. Although a number of sites have disappeared and the species is endangered in central Europe, it can still be seen in the foothills of the Alps in Austria and Germany (Alpenvorland). In Britain the Summer Lady's Treasses used to grow very rarely in wet places, once known from the New Forest in Hampshire and from the Channel Isles. In Hampshire it was last seen in 1959 and is now presumed extinct.

A British Red Data Book plant is the **Irish Lady's Tresses** (*Spiranthes romanzoffiana* Cham.). This is a short perennial with a slightly glandular-hairy stem, a dense inflorescence with many creamy or greenish white flowers in three spiral rows. It occurs in peaty areas: now in Argyllshire and in the Hebrides. Many populations, including those in Devon, have been destroyed by drainage and land reclamation. It is rare and very localised in southern Ireland.

A lovely flower of the central European meadow

steppes is the distinctive bluish violet **Purple Milk-vetch** (*Astragalus danicus* Retz.) of the Pea family (*Leguminosae*). This perennial herb issues from its branched rhizome single, sparsely branched, ascendant stems 5 to 25 cm in height. The odd-pinnate leaves, with 7—11 pairs of leaflets are covered with scattered compressed hairs. The orbicular ovate inflorescence grows in the axil of the leaves on peduncles up to over 10 cm in length. The main flowering period of this herb is late spring — May to June, but often it flowers until early autumn, although its flower is no longer so rich.

The Purple Milk-vetch is a Eurasian-continental species which also grows in North America. In central and north-western Europe it grows in warm lowland and hills on meadow steppes, in among grasses with the dominating Tor-grass, almost always in fertile black, loess, clay, loamy soils which are sometimes wet. It often spreads to secondary suitable habitats along paths, ditches and dikes. In Germany it is protected by law like many other of its genus species. In Britain the Purple Milk-vetch occurs mainly in scattered sites, usually on limestone, sometimes on coastal sand-dunes, north of the Thames. It grows in southern Scotland and in the isle of Arran off the west coast.

Even more decorative is the somewhat more xerophilous **Stemless Milk-vetch** (*Astragalus exscapus* L.) often found on rocky steppes with the Wallis Fescue. The sessile heads of bright yellow flowers grow from a false rosette of greyish, hairy pinnate leaves. The Stemless Milk-vetch flowers right up to the early autumn and is a continental species not native in Britain. It is cultivated in rock gardens.

The **Bulb-bearing Lily** (*Lilium bulbiferum* L.) of the Lily family (*Liliaceae*) is such a wonderful phe-nomenon in the central European countryside that one might wonder whether or not it is really a wild natural species. The Bulb-Bearing Lily has been cultivated as a decorative flower since time immemorial and so it is not clear which sites in central and north-western Europe are natural and which are naturalized. People often uproot it in the countryside and transfer it to their gardens. However, more damage was done to natural populations by changes in farming, particularly with the intensified use of meadows and pastures or their transformation to arable or forest land.

This perennial bulbous plant has fiery red flowers measuring 6 to 10 cm in diameter. Normally just one top flower, more rarely with 1—3 side flowers underneath it, grows on a 0.5 m high stem. They bloom from the end of spring to the end of summer from May to July. The scientific species name is derived

Distribution of the Purple Milk-vetch in Europe.

▽ The Stemless Carline Thistle (*Carlina acaulis*) with a flower head of 5 to 15 cm in diameter in the middle of a rosette of prickly leaves, is protected by law in a number of European countries; in southern Europe it is a mountain species.

The Clustered Bellflower (*Campanula glomerata*) has ▷ hairy and sometimes glabrous, unbranched stems with alternate leaves; the lower ones are stalked while the upper ones are sessile.

The Large Pink (*Dianthus superbus*), at the top of its ▷ ▷ rounded stems, has large flowers with whitish to purplish petals deeply cut into narrow pointed segments. It is sometimes found in damp, boggy meadows; elsewhere, high in the mountains.

from the dark shiny buds — bulbils — which sit in the axil of the upper narrowly lanceolate leaves by which the herb reproduces vegetatively.

The Bulb-bearing Lily is a southern European to central European species with a pre-Alpine character. This means that it is found above all in the foothills and lower mountain regions right up to over 1,500 m above sea level. At the same time, it displays a certain thermophilous tendency, growing in sunny meadows, in scrub, at wood margins and on fallow lands. There are known cases when it has even penetrated field cultures. Despite the doubts about the origin of many sites, the Bulb-bearing Lily is protected by law in many European countries. Although cultivated in gardens, the species has never been recorded in Britain as naturalized.

The **Stemless Carline Thistle** (*Carlina acaulis* L.) of the Daisy family (*Compositae*) is one of the most popular thistles. It is a very interesting and decorative one. It is often used for decorating houses and flats in winter flower arrangements.

As its English common species name indicates, the Stemless Carline Thistle has a very stunted or short decumbent or ascendant stem which is usually unbranched with one flower head. It is a variable species with a number of subspecies, varieties and forms, sometimes distinguished into separate small species. The most obvious distinguishing mark tends to be the length of the stems. The leaves are structured into a ground rosette and are about 0.25 m long, pinnatifid, tough, prickly and toothed. The inner bracts of the involucre are long, scaly and scarious with the look of ray florets. During sunny weather they open wide and when it is overcast and at night they close up. That is why the Carline Thistle is also called 'the weather forecasting thistle' ('Wetterdistel' in Germany). This perennial herb blooms

from July to September.

The plant is deeply rooted in the ground by a strong tap root which people used to dig out in autumn, wash, cut in half or into quarters and dry. The drug from this root has an unpleasant smell and a burning taste. It contains a number of effective substances of which some are constantly a subject of biochemical and pharmaceutical research. As a medicinal plant, the Stemless Carline Thistle is used for stimulating the appetite, for inflammation of the urinary tract, for encouraging a sweat with feverish illnesses and is used externally for skin diseases. It used to be a famous herb cultivated in monastery and convent gardens. Older people born in the countryside still remember how during childhood they used to pluck up strong fleshy beds of flower heads of Carline Thistle which taste like turnip or cabbage. There are records about the use of the Carline Thistles in years of bad harvests and famine. Today it is also recommended as a rewarding and resistant rock plant and is sold at specialised garden centres.

The use of the Stemless Carline Thistle as a medicinal plant or its consumption as a rather unusual vegetable cannot even be considered in central Europe today because the plant is protected by law in most countries (in Poland it is the symbol of nature conservation). Its range stretches across Europe from the Iberian Peninsula through the Alps (where there is a certain range core at an altitude of over 2,000 m above sea level) to the southern Baltic area, Belarus, and the Carpathians.

The Bellflower family (*Campanulaceae*) is represented in European meadow steppes, sunny meadows and pastures by the very decorative **Clustered Bellflower** (*Campanula glomerata* L.). The name of this perennial comes from the crowded, compact heads of rich bluish-violet 1.5 to 3 cm long flowers growing on the top of stems and in the axil of the highest leaves. It flowers throughout the summer − from June to August.

The Clustered Bellflower is a Eurasian plant with a certain southern European, sub-Mediterranean tendency. It can be found quite often from the lowlands right up to the lower mountain areas (in the Alps at about 1,800 m above sea level) in meadows of various types, mainly in the communities of the Upright Brome, the Tor-grass, the False Oat-grass etc. It grows on all kinds of ground, however always in sunny positions. A popular garden flower, it is cultivated in beds and rockeries from where it sometimes spreads. Such naturalized sites also exist in Britain. The plant, however, is native to the British flora, occurring locally as far north as Kincardine. It is rare in the western counties, in some of which it has apparently become extinct (Shropshire, for instance). It is also rare in Ireland.

Similarly, the decorative **Peach-leaved Bell-flower** (*Campanula persicifolia* L.), a plant of meadows, open woods and commons, is now only found in Britain when it spreads from gardens. It is however a British Red Data Book species, unfortunately extinct as native now, but possibly once indigenous in Devon, Surrey, Berkshire and Gloucestershire.

Intriguing too is the story of the British second 'red' bellflower − the **Rampion Bellflower** (*Campanula rapunculus* L.). This biennial used to be cultivated as a winter salad vegetable. Formerly it was widely naturalized in fields and hedgerows in England and in south Scotland. Now scattered populations exist only in Hampshire, Sussex, Surrey, Essex and Berkshire.

The **Large Pink** (*Dianthus superbus* L.) of the Pink family (*Caryophyllaceae*) is noticeable because of the unrepeatable beauty of its pale pink to light purple flowers, measuring 2 to 5 cm in diameter. The flowers are deeply (over half) laciniate, pleasantly scented and grow as one or several flowers at the end of the branch. The greyish bluish rounded stem with opposite, narrowly lanceolate leaves are up to 0.5 m high. The Large Pink flowers throughout the summer until early autumn − from June to September or the beginning of October.

The Eurasian-continental Large Pink is found in Europe (northwards to Sweden and southern Norway, but not native in Britain) in several subspecies, different not only morphologically but also with regard to their demands on the environment. The habitats of the Large Pink are dry and damp, however, usually warm, sunny and calcareous meadows, pastures and grasslands.

FIELDS AND OTHER CROP LANDS, FALLOW LAND

The European countryside is a cultivated landscape with vast fields.

The plants which we have presented so far in text and pictures, are strictly bound to certain habitats, biotopes. As we have already indicated, these habitats are being changed and destroyed, the biotopes are disappearing — and the species and entire plant communities which depend on them are also disappearing and dying. So the areas where one encounters plants in need of protection in central Europe are shrinking more and more. These areas have become more like isolated islands and islets. Man exerts his influence on the landscape and thereby obviously also affects the ecosystems. He maintains the desired ecosystems by depositing a considerable amount of energy, nutrients and various other substances into them. The supreme goal of these efforts is agricultural production, which sometimes, due to intensification, changes into over-production and this may also cause ecological problems and a crisis situation. However, the production avalanche is rapidly gathering pace. It is changing the graceful picture of the central European countryside, the mosaic of fields, meadows and small forests and all sorts of scattered nonforest verdure. Particularly in places where small-holding farming has been replaced by large-scale agriculture, extensive hundred-hectare expanses of land of short-term monocultures of agricultural crops are appearing.

It is almost unbelievable and rather paradoxical, but weeds are appearing on the red lists and in red books of many European countries. Suddenly people are beginning to wonder how to save from extinction plants against which, until recently, they had led a merciless struggle and for the destruction of which they kept coming up with more sophisticated methods and products.

So we should be pleased that we have finally almost got rid of weeds. These are plants of various, sometimes even of unknown or at least disputed origin, introduced together with agriculture from other continents or even 'cultivated' by agriculture almost as a by-product. There are direct specialists among weeds; in central Europe these are particularly the so-called linicolous weeds related to the flax culture. These have been destroyed almost without a trace because flax is cultivated today to a much lesser extent, and moreover with such agricultural technology that this weed is completely suppressed.

However, even weeds have begun to be conserved. The goal of species conservation is to try to prevent the complete extinction of any species. Each plant species is part of a large plant genetic fund base and so far we cannot definitely proclaim that it was, is and will be totally useless or even harmful.

At first there was uncertainty as to how to solve this problem, but not for long. Matters were taken into hand by open-air museums — museums of folk architecture and the traditional ways of life of former generations. The preservation and systematic protection of plant life is also organically incorporated into the museums' tasks: the protection of old cultural varieties of disappearing and forgotten fruit and decorative wood plants, often only local varieties of agricultural crops, useful plants, decorative flowers and also weed and ruderal plants. (Ruderal plants form long- and short-term communities mainly on urban sites which have been disturbed or altered by man such as road verges and ditches, barren land, wasteland or various forgotten village nooks.) A pioneer role in this area of species conservation, even in international cooperation, is played by the Rhenish open-air museum (Rheinisches Freilichtmuseum) in Kommern, south-west of Bonn. However, one can also find 'biogenetic' corners and plant conservation on other facilities of this type.

The cockle has become a direct symbol of the weed, although very few of today's younger generation have actually seen this plant. The **Corn-Cockle** (*Agrostemma githago* L.) has accompanied human cultures since time immemorial. Archaeological research in northern Switzerland has proved that the Corn-Cockle has been a companion of farming since the late stone age (the Neolithic period).

It is quite an attractive annual herb which clearly belongs to the Pink family (*Caryophyllaceae*). The medium to tall, greyish, hairy herb has erect stems which are slightly branched in the top parts. The linear lanceolate, pointed leaves are up to 10 cm long with three protruding nerves. The flower has obovate dull purple sepals which exceed the length of the linear lobes of the green calyx. The large flowers measure 3-4 cm in diameter and appear from June to September. The fruit is an elongated ovate hard capsule about 2 cm long. It contains about 40 relatively large (2.5 − 3.5 mm) black or dark brown seeds.

As a weed, the Corn-Cockle has spread across farm lands throughout the world. It is generally supposed that it is of Mediterranean origin, where certain other species of the genus also occur such as the **Greek Tender Cockle** (*Agrostemma gracilis* Boiss) which is on the European botanical red list. The Corn-Cockle is an undemanding plant with regard to its habitat, its roots stretch down over 1 m in depth and it grows from lowlands to 1,000 m above sea level on lower mountain slopes. It has adapted to agricultural cultures and has become a dangerous weed

▽ The mosaic of the landscape, although ecologically balanced and scenically attractive, can no longer be imagined without human settlements and farming lands.

The Corn-Cockle (*Agrostemma githago*) is an attractive ▷ herb with conspicuous, long lobes of a greenish-greyish, woolly calyx. It is on the decline.

The Tassel Hyacinth (*Muscari comosum*) with a crest ▷ ▷ of sterile, bluish violet flowers at the end of the raceme. Originally a species of rock and grass steppes, it occasionally colonizes secondary habitats in man-made ecosystems.

The Summer Pheasant's-eye (*Adonis aestivalis*) has ▷ ▽ blackish violet stamens in a bright red, sometimes yellow, flower, and leaves pinnately cut into linear segments. A Mediterranean species, it is treated as a weed further north and it is rapidly declining now.

particularly to cereals. As such, it is a characteristic species of the class of plant associations of cereal weeds called *Secalinetea.*

In central and western Europe the Corn-Cockle has evolved into a very specialised and difficult weed, its biology narrowly related to the biologies of cultural winter wheat crops particularly cereals and the Fodder Vetch (*Vicia villosa*). The seeds (one plant can bear about 300) cease to germinate in the soil within about a year, but if put into dry storage then they will last about 10 years. It used to find its way into a field by being incorporated in a badly cleaned batch of sowing seeds, germinated in the autumn, created a ground rosette of leaves which hibernated and fully developed in the second year together with the culture crop. Already by early

spring, the plants of the cockle would stifle the crops both above and under ground. Then together with the fodder (winter vetch or other crops), they were mowed, thus deteriorating the food value of the crop in both the fresh and dry state. The cockle is poisonous, containing saponins. The most feared parts were the seeds which are dangerous both to animals and man. Badly cleaned corn and tailings used to cause poisoning. Insufficiently cleaned grain was milled into flour, but it takes just a 5% content of cockle seeds to make them dangerous to health. From about the first quarter of this century the cleaning of grain has improved considerably with the use of special machines and since that time the cockle has been disappearing from the fields of central and western Europe.

Today the cockle is a rare sight. In British cornfields the Corn-Cockle was still abundant after World War II. It has declined considerably in recent years due to cleaner agricultural seed and the use of herbicides. Only occasionally it reappears today in disturbed and former arable fields. Some permanent sites have survived in eastern England and in Moray. The Corn-Cockle is a British Red Data Book species. So one would probably only see the once feared and today artificially maintained cockle in a botanical garden or open-air museum. It is not only an interesting exhibit, but also quite a decorative flower.

The **Tassel Hyacinth** (*Muscari comosum* (L.) Mill) belongs to the Lily family (*Liliaceae*) and to the hyacinth relationship as indicated by its English name. It is a perennial herb with underground bulbs and is usually 0.5 m high when in flower. The leaves are broadly linear and long. The inflorescence — a sparse elongated raceme — contains 40 to 100 flowers. The lower flowers are short-stalked, brownish and green at the edges and nearly 1 cm long. The

middle flowers are smaller, bluish, usually nodding. The upper violet blue flowers on long stalks are sterile and form an attractive terminal tuft — hence the plant's scientific species name. The Tassel Hyacinth flowers from spring to summer, most often from May to July.

The Tassel Hyacinth is a Mediterranean species, but apart from southern Europe, it also grows in north Africa and western Asia. In central Europe it grows locally in warm regions. It is a native species of the rock and grass steppes of southern and central parts of Germany, warm and dry regions of the Czech and Slovak Republics and Austria, but also penetrates grassland at the roads, verges, ditches, banks, and as a weed in vineyards and cornfields. It is difficult to determine whether the occurrence is na-

◁ The Nigella (*Nigella arvensis*) has five pale bluish green, heart-shaped and pointed petal-like sepals; the actual petals are transformed into yellowish green nectaries; also green are the numerous stamens and the 3 to 8 pistils.

The Annual Androsace (*Androsace maxima*) belongs ▽ to the Primrose family (*Primulaceae*). From the basal leafy rosette grow several flower-bearing scapes, the middle ones are erect, the side ones ascendant; the large set of bracts around the umbel of flowers increases in size after the plant has flowered.

Fields, or fully cultivated formations, are ecosystems ▷ which combine both the cultivated plants and some 'undesirable guests', among which endangered species can also appear.

The Wall Bedstraw (*Galium parisiense*) is an incon- ▷ ▽ spicuous plant which can easily be mistaken for other Bedstraws: its leaves are single-veined and the flowers in axil panicles are reddish outside.

tive or not as the Tassel Hyacinth is cultivated in gardens (also in certain cultivated decorative varieties) from which it sometimes spreads. In central Europe it is listed in various threat categories on several red lists, in some countries (for example in Germany) it is protected by law. The areas of occurrence in Britain have all resulted from garden cultivation: in south Wales the Tassel Hyacinth is reported to be naturalized.

Several further species of hyacinths occur in central Europe and all are more clearly native plants of dry grasslands of a steppe character. Today they are endangered species on the decline and therefore in need of protection.

The British Red Data Book includes the **Grape Hyacinth** (*Muscari atlanticum* Boiss. et Reut.), a very variable short, hairless perennial with linear lcaves and dark blackish blue flowers in a fairly dense spike-like raceme. The Grape Hyacinth flowering in March — May occurs in dry grassland and in hedgerows in cultivated ground and occasionally in rubbish tips in Suffolk and Cambridgeshire; it is extinct in Norfolk.

The yellow beauty of the spring steppe, the Yellow Pheasant's Eye, has its less attractive poor relations among European weeds. They too — although not protected by law — have found themselves in various categories on central and western European red lists. These thermophilous companions of agricultural cultures dislike modern agricultural technology and cannot stand the considerable use of chemicals in modern farming. Otherwise, like most members of the Buttercup family (*Ranunculaceae*), they too are poisonous. The German folk name 'Teufelsauge' (Devil's Eye) highlights the contradiction between the beauty of the plant and its poisonousness. However, like the Yellow Pheasant's Eye,

the Small Weed Pheasant's Eyes also contain substances with curative effects.

The **Summer Pheasant's-eye** (*Adonis aestivalis* L.) is an annual, 25 to 50 cm high herb with an erect, sparsely branched lengthways carved stem. The leaves are three to four pinnate in linear segments. The individual flowers, on the end of the stems, measure 1.5 to 3.5 cm in diameter, and have very conspicuous bright scarlet (only rarely yellowish) petals numbering 6 to 8. The summer adonis flowers at the end of spring and beginning of the summer — from May to July.

It is a European/western Siberian species, also widespread in the mountains of North Africa. In central and western Europe it can only be found as a weed usually being brought in with seeds. It grows

in warm lowlands, hill country and lower mountain areas (in the foothills of the Jura up to an altitude of about 1,000 m above sea level) on mainly fertile, calcareous, stony, clay, loam and even sandy soils. It accompanies cereals mainly as a characteristic species of the weed plant association of the Small Bur-parsley (*Caucalis platycarpos*) and the Summer and Flaming Pheasant's-eyes (*Caucalido adonidetum*). However, it can occasionally be found on fallow land, at roadsides, in hedgerows and on embankments.

The Summer Pheasant's-eye does not occur in Britain. Only one of the thermophilous weed species of the genus — the **Pheasant's-eye** (*Adonis annua* L.) — does and it is very rare in British cereal crops. It has three pinnated leaves and bright scarlet flowers with conspicuous black centres.

The **Nigella** (*Nigella arvensis* L.) belongs to the same Buttercup family (*Ranunculaceae*). It is an annual, completely bluish green herb 10 to 30 cm high. The erect stems are densely branched with leaves or three pinnate in linear segments. The petals are altered to bilabiate yellowish green nectaries. The calyx is made up of heart-like, pointed, whitish, bluish, green stained and reticulate sepals. The plant flowers throughout summer, from June to September.

The Nigella is of Mediterranean origin. It was brought into central and western Europe as a weed with spring corn, fodder plants and root-crops. It grows on warm, sunny sites in fertile, mainly calcareous soils in which it takes root to a depth of over 0.5 m. The seeds used to be used as a spice — as indicated by the plants's German common name 'black caraway'. Modern farming technology has almost completely forced the Nigella out of farm cultures.

So this once rather abundant field and ruderal weed has become a rarity in warmer regions. On central European red lists it is classed under the higher threat categories. In Britain it is sparse in the wild, but it is occasionally cultivated in gardens. In view of the fact that the Nigella contains saponins, essential oil, mustard oil and tannin, it represents a valuable genetic resource whose extinction would certainly be a loss.

The related and similar **Common Nigella** (*Nigella sativa* L.) is an even more rare thermophilous weed. It is cultivated as an aromatic and medicinal plant, the seeds being used as a drug. It is used to treat intestinal diseases and illnesses of the biliary duct, flatulence, bronchitis, inflammation of the upper respiratory system and intestinal parasites. In open-air

museums one can also find another representative of this genus — called the **Love-in-a-mist** (*Nigella damascena* L.) — but it cannot be found among weeds, ruderal or medicinal plants. It is a more robust herb with larger whitish flowers. It used to be a popular ornamental plant in traditional gardens.

The **Annual Androsace** (*Androsace maxima* L.) belongs to the Primrose family (*Primulaceae*). This short, hairy, annual herb is distinguished by its ground rosette of ovate, toothed, slightly fleshy leaves. The scape is 2 to 5 cm high and carries umbels of whitish or pinkish 5 or more flowers in a set of bracts, flowering from April to May.

The Annual Androsace is a Eurasian-continental to Mediterranean species. It is sometimes found in central and western Europe (but not in Britain) as a field and ruderal weed on warm and sunny sites. It grows in sandy soils with little humus. Today it is either critically endangered or altogether extinct (in Germany and the Czech Republic).

Many representatives of weed and ruderal flora can be found in the Bedstraws (*Galium*) of the Bedstraw family (*Rubiaceae*). Some of them grow abundantly in these habitats and spread quickly. The sewage from excessively fertilized fields enourages the development of so-called nitrophilous species, i.e. withstanding or even demanding an abundance of nitrogenous substances. However, other weed bedstraws are very much on the decline in central and western Europe. One of these is the **Wall Bedstraw** (*Galium parisiense* L.), extinct in Germany and critically endangered elsewhere.

The Wall Bedstraw is an annual, only 5 to 25 cm high herb with a four-sided, densely branched and bristly herbaceous stem. The linear lanceolate leaves of 4 − 6 whorls are also bristly. The axil and top cymes are made up of tiny greenish, yellowish flowers which are a reddish colour on the outer part. The flowers bloom from June to September.

The centre of this species' range is the northern Mediterranean and the more temperate regions of western Europe within reach of the oceanic climate. The Wall Bedstraw grows on stony and derelict sites, on fallow land, on verges and field borders in dry and sandy soils. Sometimes it is also found in communities of field weeds, particularly cereal weeds. Today in central Europe — unless already extinct — it is a great rarity.

In Britain the Wall Bedstraw is rare and extremely localised, occurring in south-eastern England and East Anglia.

Bedstraws are a valuable genetic resource. They contain some remarkable substances, particularly

glycosides for which some species have been picked for many years and are still gathered as medicinal plants. The stalk is used against urinary tract illnesses and cramp, and externally for treating wounds, burns, rashes and ulcers. The German name 'Lab-kraut' (laben = to curdle) derives from the fact that the plant's leaves contain ferment which curdles milk. Hence formerly bedstraws were used in the production of cheese.

The **Grass Vetchling** (*Lathyrus nissolia* L.) is an annual, bald green herb with simple, erect, 20—50 cm long herbaceous stems. The leaves have linear spread rachises and small drooping stipules. The red or violet flowers, measuring almost 1 cm in diameter, at first sight look as if they are related to the sweet pea of the Pea family (*Leguminosae*). It flowers from the beginning of summer — in June and July.

The Grass Vetchling is mainly found in the Mediterranean region. In central and western Europe there are two types of habitat: it grows as a native species on the verges of dry meadows and forests. As a weed it appears in cereal fields, at the borders of agricultural land, roadsides and semi-ruderal hedgerows. It is a thermophilous and xerophilous plant. It is very rare in both types of habitat, endangered by the effects of human activity. It appears on several central European red lists in various threat categories together with other types of similar character. For example there is the **Yellow Vetchling** (*Lathyrus aphaca* L.), a greyish green herb with colourful yellowish violet flowers and leaves that usually develop only into stipules, and the **Hairy**

Vetchling (*Lathyrus hirsutus* L.), a rather robust plant with up to 1 m high herbaceous stems and colourful (violet, pink, whitish, veined) flowers, measuring over 1 cm in diameter. All the above mentioned vetchlings are localised and declining in Britain. Probably all of them are also only naturalized.

The attractive **Orlaya** (*Orlaya grandiflora* (L.) Hoffm.) of the Carrot family (*Apiaceae*) is an annual, 10—50 cm high herb. Remarkable and highly decorative are the strongly radiate outer flowers in an umbel with white or pinkish corollas about 1 cm long. It flowers throughout the whole summer.

The Orlaya is a native species in the Mediterranean. It penetrates central and western Europe sporadically in warm, sunny calcareous lowlands and hills. The most northerly points of this range are the rocky steppes on the shell limestone in Thuringia, eastern Germany (in danger of extinction, in Saxony-Anhalt already extinct) and the rocky steppes on the sunny limestone hillsides in the Biosphere Reserve of Pálava, southern Moravia in the Czech Republic (threatened species on the red list) which sometimes, during flowering, literally glows white with thousands of rays. This important Czech biogenetic reserve is one guarantee that the species will be conserved in a natural biotope in central Europe.

The thermophilous and xerophilous Orlaya is dependent on calcareous soil with a clay content in which it roots about 0.75 m in depth. Sometimes and ever more rarely it appears in warm regions as a weed in corn fields and on fallow land.

SCRUBS, BROADLEAF WOODS, THEIR MARGINS AND GLADES

Many attractive wild flowers grow in open thermophilous oak woods; a wood in the Pannonian region with a flowering White Dittany (*Dictamnus albus*).

It is ever more apparent that the forests of the European temperate zone form a truly unique biome (i.e. a major ecological community over a large area and usually characterised by a dominant vegetation) in the world. Even today the forests of central Europe cover about one quarter of its area — which is much more than elsewhere on the European continent, with the exception of northern and eastern Europe. The total area covered by forest in Switzerland, Austria, Germany, the Czech and Slovak Republics, Poland and Hungary is over a quarter of a million square kilometres. Apart from their importance as regards timber production, forests also contribute towards creating an ecologically favourable system in the central European countryside. Their non-productive, social functions are becoming more and more significant today. The importance of forest units for recreational purposes is increasing with the deteriorating environment, urbanization and industrialization of the countryside. The perception of the aesthetic function of forests and the resulting recognition of aesthetic aims in forest management has been incorporated into Czech, Slovak, German, Austrian, Slovenian and Swiss forestry schools and training centres for some time.

The state of central European forests however does not really correspond to the natural conditions. Barely a third of forest growth in the heart of Europe can be considered as close to natural woodland communities. Growths of equal age, far removed from natural conditions, which are of one tree species — monocultures (e.g. the Spruce, Pine) — were planted by forest managers in the last 150 years on extensive stretches of the north German lowland, in the Polish lowlands, in hills and in the Alpine foothills (the Alpenvorland): the situation is much better in the Carpathians. In the last century in the Pannon-ian region and its promontories entire groves of False Acacia were created which were totally exotic to central Europe, having been introduced from North America. Nevertheless, in Hungary the Acacia, thanks to man, became one of the most widespread of forest wood plants. The urbanised and industrialised central European man is led to think that the artificial forest ecosystems are the real forests, while the remains of the original and natural islets of broad-leaf woodlands are regarded as being some sort of 'wild' shrublands which, in the interest of order and yield, should be nicely arranged into rows of uniform spruces.

In this chapter we will deal with the region of mixed European oak woods, by looking at several selected plant species which are most in need of conservation, to preserve the great diversity, colour, wealth and beauty of their flora. Immediately after the beech, the second most widespread woody plant of European deciduous woodland its the oak. Old forest managers encouraged the growth of deciduous forests. Nevertheless, they used them for extensive cattle grazing, they raked the leaves for litter or for other purposes or they used them as coppices, i.e. they periodically cut the trunks and stems growing from the 'eternal' tree stumps. To modern managers, deciduous trees represented a waste of space. They grew too slowly and the building or any other industrial sector (particularly pulp mills) were not as interested in their timber as they were in the straight spruce and pine trunks. Only after the Second World War many forest managers, having learnt from insect calamities, the soil deterioriation under the monocultures and the consequences of the drought year of 1947, began to propagate, plant, test and implement a return to mixed forests and to the renewed promotion of deciduous trees.

Mixed oak woods are very diverse in Europe. In warm and dry regions remnants can still be found of thermophilous oak woods with the rare White Oak (*Quercus pubescens* Willd.) with its young densely hairy shoots and young leaves. In north-western, western and central Europe acid oak woods are dominated by the Sessile Oak (*Quercus petraea* (Mattuschka) Liebl.) and Penduculate Oak (*Quercus robur* L.), with a strong mixture of birches. However, their flora is not as rich as that one of the thermophilous oak woods. From the lowlands through hills to the highland areas the hornbeam oak woods prevail in which the Common Hornbeam (*Carpinus betulus* L.) associates a lot with the above mentioned two species. The drastic changes, already described, in the structure of forest growths ruthlessly eliminated the colourful woodland, but the new and innovative guidelines in forest management provide new hope. New space and possibilities can be created for threatened species of deciduous woodland. For example in the Rhineland there have been successful efforts to cultivate mixed oak groves

by reclaiming areas devastated by open-pit coal mining.

In Britain there is a considerably lower percentage of woodland than in other European countries. The decrease is, of course, the work of man, and the only precious, unaffected woodland to be found is in some isolated patches in Scotland, with very few in England and Wales. A small area, carefully managed over many centuries, still persists in East Anglia and some other places. After the establishment of the Forestry Commission in 1919, large new forests were planted and a large proportion of woods changed. But those forests consist mainly of regular rows of spruce and other fast-growing conifers, often not native ones. Conservation authorities and voluntary organisations are now strongly supporting the conservation of natural and semi-natural woodland with its rich and interesting flora by establishing Nature Reserves and other protected areas as well as by launching various Wildlife Enhancement schemes, various grants, etc.

In central European towns and cities **Snowdrop** (*Galanthus nivalis* L.) has become the symbol of the arrival of spring. The Snowdrop is a delicate bulbous perennial of the Daffodil family (*Amaryllidaceae*). It flowers in February or March, and later in higher latitudes, and soon closes up. The herb is about 10 to 20 cm high with narrow, greyish green, slightly fleshy leaves with one flower at the end of a scape on a nodding, thin stalk. The scented flower, 1.5 to 2 cm in length, has a compound perianth with two groups of segments: the three outer ones are larger and all white, the inner segments are smaller and in the middle of the flower they create a sort of inner small bell with greenish spots on the tips.

In Europe the Snowdrop can mostly be found in the southern part (with an island range in western

France) and does not reach the northern lowlands. In the open countryside it grows in open woodland, from alluvial, damp, regularly flooded woods, in thermophilous white oak and horn beam oak groves to fresh foothill and mountain beech woods, in deep, fertile clay and loam soils, elsewhere also in humous fine scree.

In the European landscape the Snowdrop is a rather dynamic species. It also has secondary occurrences in meadows. It is a popular garden plant cultivated for its pleasant spring flower and it has spread from gardens. Its garden culture is ancient, and so today botanists claim that, in Germany, the natural, native occurrences of the Snowdrop are only in the southern part of western Germany, while all sites from Bavaria northwards are of naturalized origin. It has become naturalized in England, Wales, Scotland and Ireland, Belgium and the Netherlands and even in Scandinavia. In view of the fact that it is a popular flower for vases and in gardens, people

persistently dig it up in the open countryside. It has partly or altogether disappeared from many areas and even entire regions of its former range, for example in the Czech and Slovak Republics or Austria. It is protected by law in Germany, Switzerland and Austria.

Within the scope of present efforts regarding active non-traditional conservation of threatened species, individual plants are being transferred from unavoidably endangered habitats to safe susbstitute habitats. Either municipal parks or suburban recreational forests provide a good opportunity for this. Attempts are also being undertaken to reintroduce Snowdrops back to habitats where they once became extinct, but where suitable biotopes have remained. These efforts possess one snag: care must be taken of the genetic purity of the transplanted plants.

A very decorative gardeners' favourite, and hence often stolen from the open countryside, is the low bush with early spring flowers called **Scented Daphne** (*Daphne cneorum* L.). It grows to a height of 10 to 25 cm. The procumbent to ascendant branches are densely leafed, with evergreen, tough, elongated alternating leaves. The flower-bearing branches carry dense umbels of dark pink four-part flowers which give off a strong carnation scent. They flower, depending on the site, from April to June.

The Scented Daphne is a European species. It grows sporadically from the Pyrenees right up to the foothills of the Caucasus. There is a certain concentration of occurence in the Alpine region. In central Europe the Scented Daphne grows in steppe grasslands, on rocky hillsides, in open woodland (but usually in calciphilous pine woods rather than in oak groves) and in lower altitudes (up to about 2,000 m above sea level) of the Swiss, German and Austrian Alps (mainly in valleys along which it descends to

Distribution of the Erect Clematis in Europe.

▽ The Variegated Iris (*Iris variegata*) grows on rock steppes, but mainly in thermophilous oak woods, on their margins and in glades. The outer drawn back perianth segments are 4 to 6 cm long with a little yellow brush and brown or dark violet veins.

The Multicoloured Spurge (*Euphorbia polychroma*) ↱ has conspicuous, yellowish orange supporting bracts in its inflorescence. The erect, hairy stems are quite densely leafed and form tufts.

The Purple Mullein (*Verbascum phoeniceum*) has dark ▷ ▷ violet, large flowers in a long, but lax raceme; they bloom gradually from the bottom to the top of the inflorescence which is never entirely in full flower.

alluvial gravel banks). It colonizes habitats with shallow, stony, calcareous soils or even sands. It is a thermophilous species growing in full sunlight and in semi-shade. The northern border of its range passes through the Czech and Slovak Republics where it is a great rarity.

The Scented Daphne is a poisonous plant. It is threatened by deliberate uprooting due to its very decorative appearance and by the destruction of its habitats. The steppe grasslands are being transformed into vineyards and other agricultural cultures, open pine woods become uniform with the increased industrialization of forest management. In all central European countries it is protected by law.

The **Erect Clematis** (*Clematis recta* L.) belongs to the Buttercup family (*Ranunculaceae*). It is a robust, over 1 m high perennial herb. At the end of spring (May-June) it is conspicuous with its rich top cymes of flowers whose petals are missing, but the 1.5 cm long, white sepals resemble them. In the summer (July-August) it has decorative fruits — achenes with 2 cm long, feathery awns. The large opposite leaves are odd-pinnate with 2 to 4 pairs of leaflets.

The centre of the Erect Clematis range lies in the eastern European deciduous woods and in the north of the Mediterranean region. The north-western border of its range passes through central Europe. It is a thermophilous and xerophilous species. It grows in regions of xerotherm flora on sunny bushy hillsides, sometimes even on rocky steppes, but mainly in forest steppes, in white oak woods, in their glades and on their margins. The western border of its geographical distribution runs across Germany and France. The Erect Clematis is naturalized in Norway, but does not occur in Britain.

Central Europe lies on the western and northern border of the range of the very decorative **Varie-**

gated Iris (*Iris variegata* L.) of the Iris family (*Iridaceae*). It is a 20—40 cm high perennial with a thick rhizome. The sword-like leaves are almost as long as the flower bearing stem. The flowers are pale to golden yellow with brown and violet veins and bloom from May to June.

The Variegated Iris is one of the prettiest wild European species of its family. It is cultivated as an ornamental flower in gardens, so it is sometimes difficult to determine, particularly on the border of its range, whether the locality is an indigenous or a secondary

one. The Iris was adored and cultivated by the ancient Greeks. The genus was named after Iris, the Greek goddess of the rainbow. In recent years the Iris has made a come-back as a popular decorative flower. Hundreds of varieties have resulted from hybridization and cultivation of this plant. The basic, starting material is a natural genetic resource.

Hungary has the largest nature reservoir of the Variegated Iris in central Europe. It grows there in thermophilous oak woods in glades and on the margins in the hills of the central and northern parts of the country. It penetrates steppe grasslands and rock steppes and there are known occurrences in the secondary pusztas on the loess and sands. In spite of the fact that it grows there in relative abundance, often in the extensive colonies of plants reproducing vegetatively, the Variegated Iris is endangered by the felling of forests and the change in their structure, the grazing and trampling by game and mass recreation in the wild.

The Variegated Iris spreads from Hungary west towards Austria and the southern part of Germany right up to the Jura and the basin of Lake Constance. Its northern border runs through the southernmost parts of the Czech and Slovak Republics. In the south it grows as far as the Balkan peninsula and eastward as far as the Black Sea.

The lovely **Multicoloured Spurge** (*Euphorbia epithomoides* L., syn. *E. polychroma* Kern) of the spurge family (*Euphorbiaceae*) is also cultivated in gardens as a decorative flower. The German common name 'Wolfmilch' (wolf's milk) derives from the white milky juice which the plant releases when wounded and which contains the poison euphorbon. The Multicoloured Spurge is a perennial herb. From a thick multi-headed rhizome erect, soft and hairy 30 to 50 cm high stems grow every year in a relatively dense, basket-like tuft. In the lower part they bear reddish scales and higher up they are densely covered by alternating, elongated, soft hairy leaves. The flowers are tiny in the top umbels. The most conspicuous and ornamental parts of the plant are the bracts which, during flowering (May — June), are a yellowish orange colour.

The Multicoloured Spurge is a European and eastern Mediterranean species. The northern border of its range runs through Moravia and Slovakia. It is a thermophilous plant, growing in sunny or semi-shaded habitats, on stony or clay calcareous soils in thermophilous oak woods, in scrub on hillsides, in forest steppes, woodland margins and glades.

There are four Spurges included in the British Red Data Book, two of them occurring in warm open deciduous woods. Unfortunately, one of them, the **Hairy Spurge** (*Euphorbia villosa* Waldst. et Kit.), became extinct around 1900. This rather stout perennial with numerous stems and flowers in umbel-like clusters was recorded as early as in 1576 in a wood in Somerset. The wood was managed by coppicing and this was good for the species; the greatest population size was observed just after clearance. As the brushwood grew up, the numbers decreased, and finally, cessation of coppicing led to the species' extinction.

The second British Red Data Book Spurge is the **Upright Spurge** (*Euphorbia serrulata* Thuill.), a small and slender hairless annual or biennial, found very rarely in woodland clearings on limestone in Gloucestershire and Monmouthshire.

The Mulleins are robust but graceful herbs with a candlestick-like inflorescence of yellow flowers. However, one European wild species has an attractive lax inflorescence of violet flowers. This is the **Purple Mullein** (*Verbascum phoeniceum* L.) which is an annual, biennial or even a perennial with a ground rosette and usually with a branchless, sparsely leafed stem about 0.5 m high. The flowers in the top raceme have dark violet, sometimes brownish, more rarely reddish and even more rarely white rotate corolla of 2.5 to 3 cm in diameter. They flower gradually from the end of spring to the beginning of summer, from May to July.

In view of its geographic distribution, the Purple Mullein is also a European/west Siberian species. The north-western border of its range runs through central Europe and its most extreme point is Brandenburg. The origin of its occurrence in the Rhineland is a problem as the Purple Mullein in southern Germany is regarded as having been introduced. Nevertheless, on the German red list it is classed as a species in the highest threat category. In Austria it is found only in Lower Austria, in Styria next to the Hungarian border and in several locations in Corinthia and the Tyrol. It is a thermophilous and xerophilous species of open woods and their margins, of bushy hillsides, but also of open steppes, rock steppes and warm sands.

Mulleins, plants of the Figwort family (*Scrophulariaceae*), contain precious substances and so some of the species are picked or even cultivated as medicinal plants. The Purple Mullein is not a medicinal plant, but is cultivated for its beauty and sometimes appears in the wild having spread from gardens. It is protected by law in the Czech Republic.

The Purple Mullein is not native in the British flora. Among seven species occurring in Britain, two rare ones were considered for inclusion into the British Red Data Book, but finally discarded. Both of them occur on waste grounds rather than in woodlands. The **Twiggy Mullein** (*Verbascum virgatum* Stokes) is a medium to tall biennial, with yellow flowers in small clusters of 2–5 along the raceme. It is restricted to Devon, Cornwall and the Isles of Scilly, as well as Ireland. The mealy-white **Hoary Mullein** (*Verbascum pulverulentum* Vill.) with large (up to 2.5 cm) yellow flowers in large pyramidal panicles is restricted to a few areas in Norfolk and Suffolk.

One of the species whose native occurrence in central Europe is disputable because it is often cultivated in gardens from where it spreads, is the **Wreathshaped Ragged Robin** (*Lychnis coronaria* (L.) Desr.) of the Pink family (*Caryophyllaceae*). It is a perennial 50 cm – 1 m high herb covered in white hairs, with ground rosettes of leaves and tough stems, which are densely branched in the upper part. The richly crimson flowers with five petals bloom from June to September.

The Wreathshaped Ragged Robin is native in south-eastern Europe and Asia Minor. The northern border of its range runs through southern Slovakia where the plant is protected by law. It is also protected in Switzerland where it grows wild only in the bend of the river Rhône at Martigny in Valais. It is a thermophilous species of fertile if often stony soils in warm regions of oak woods. However, it also grows a lot on open grassland or rocky sites which have had their forest cover removed. The Wreathshaped Ragged Robin has been cultivated as a decorative flower in country gardens since at least the 16th century.

▽ ◁ The Purple Ragged Robin (*Lychnis coronaria*) has abundant, sparsely branched stems at the base of the branches; dark scarlet flowers of 2 to 3 cm in diameter grow on thin stalks.

◁ The Bastard Balm (*Melittis melissophyllum*) is easily identified by its conspicuous, whitish purple two-lipped flowers at the base of the upper leaves.

The Lady's Slipper Orchid (*Cypripedium calceolus*) is ▽ the only wild European orchid which, in the size, shape and colour of its flowers, can fully compare to tropical orchids. It grows in the undergrowth of deciduous, mixed and coniferous woods.

The Violet Bird's Nest Orchid (*Limodorum abortivum*) ▷ is a rare European orchid without green leaves: the steel bluish violet flowers rarely open up fully.

Among its protected native species, Switzerland has another decorative plant which is also cultivated in gardens elsewhere in Europe. This is the **Jovis Ragged Robin** (*Lychnis flos-jovis* (L.) Desr.). This is shorter, usually about 0.5 m in height, with long, pointed leaves and pinkish-reddish, crimson or white flowers. It is found very rarely in open woods and meadows in lower southern Alps.

The **Bastard Balm** (*Melittis melissophyllum* L.) of the Mint family (*Lamiaceae*) has a conspicuous shape and colour and the flowers have a particularly wonderful scent. This perennial, soft, hairy herb grows to a height of 20 to 40 cm. The opposite leaves are short-stalked, broadly ovate, coarsely toothed and stick out of the herbaceous stem almost vertically. At the base of upper leaves several 2—4 cm long whitish pink flowers grow (in clusters of 2—6) on long thin stalks. They bloom at the end of spring and beginning of summer — in May and June.

This is a southern European species. It is however quite common in central and western Europe in light and dry deciduous woodland, in forest steppes, various types of oak woods, hornbeam oak woods and beech woods from lowlands up to highlands, in the mountains and in northern regions primarily on calcareous ground. Although in Europe it is protected by law only in the Czech Republic and Switzerland, it deserves protection elsewhere because due to all sorts of effects of civilization on woodland, it is on the decline. People also pick it a lot, either for its decorative appearance or because they think that it is a medicinal plant due to its honey scent. Sometimes it is also cultivated in gardens for decoration.

In Britain the Bastard Balm occurs locally in shady habitats in woodland margins and hedgerows in south England from the New Forest to Devon and Cornwall, and also in western Wales. It is considered a rare and threatened species, but not so much so that be listed in the British Red Data Book.

Among the flora of the woods and scrubs, one also comes across the aristocracy of European flora — wild orchids. In earlier chapters we mentioned that their flowers are only miniatures of the large tropical orchid flowers we know and see in greenhouses or florists' shops. There are only a few European orchids whose flowers can measure up in size to tropical ones. In the first place there is an absolutely wonderful species — the **Lady's Slipper Orchid** (*Cypripedium calceolus* L.).

This perennial herb grows from 20 to 60 cm when

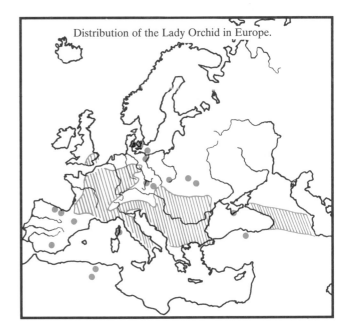

Distribution of the Lady Orchid in Europe.

in flower. The stems, growing from a short articulated ground rhizome, are hairy with three to four alternating, sessile, ovate to lanceolate leaves. Flowers, most often solitary, sometimes two, very rarely three, grow at the base of scaly bracts at the top of stems. Normally these flowers have brownish red, sometimes yellowish or greenish perianth segments and a conspicuous, large yellow inflated lip which resembles a slipper; hence all the scientific and folk names of the plant. The flowers bloom at the end of spring — in May and June — and, at a size of up to 8 cm in diameter, they are one of the largest flowers of European plants.

The Lady's Slipper flower is in fact a refined insect trap. The bright yellow lip attracts insects which sit on it and easily slip down the smooth edges inside. The insects can't get out again because the walls are steep and covered by an oily, slippery substance. The only way out for these involuntary prisoners are 'windows', openings in the side walls in the bottom part of the lip which are penetrated by the light, thereby attracting the insect. Because getting out of the flower is not easy, the insect rubs its back against the anther and takes away on his body the sticky pollen. Then it falls into the next flower and, in freeing itself, rubs the pollen against the nodding stigma. So the trap of the slipper flower is in fact a device for the pollination of the plant. The insect does not benefit at all from this because the flower does not offer it any food. We call this sort of flower a deceptive flower.

The Lady's Slipper is a circumpolar orchid growing in the temperate zone of Eurasia and North America. It occurs as far north as the Arctic Circle. It can be found in the western part of Europe growing as far as England, in the north up to Scandinavia and into the northern regions of the Baltic

Republics and Russia but in the south only as far as northern Italy and the northern part of the Balkans.

This orchid is relatively rare, but is found in various types of habitats. It grows on sunny, semi-shaded and even shaded sites. However, it is calciphilous and requires good decomposed humus. It is mainly found in deciduous woodland — oak woods, hornbeam oak woods and beech woods, but it can also be found in coniferous forests — in hills in pine woods on limestone, in foothills and in the north spruce woods. In lowlands and hills it also appears on bushy hillsides, even above the upper forest limit in the dwarf pine belt. Nevertheless it does show certain slight thermophilous tendencies because it is found in regions with mainly warm summers. In central Europe it grows in the Tyrol up to 1,700 m above sea level, in the German Alps up to almost 1,500 m above sea level. In Slovakia it is common in Carpathians up to an altitude of 800 to 1,200 m above sea level, and in the limestone Belianské Tatras of the Tatra National Park it grows even higher.

The Lady's Slipper is a very attractive decorative flower often cultivated in gardens, especially in rock gardens. People uproot it from the wild, so it is greatly endangered and has become extinct in some habitats. (Despite the fact that the specimens of this and several other equally beautiful botanical species can be obtained relatively easily from commercial gardeners.) In Belgium and Luxembourg the Lady's Slipper Orchid has become extinct; in Britain it is critically endangered. It is included on the European red list and is carefully protected throughout Europe. In many cases its occurrences have motivated the establishment of protected territories, mostly of the Nature Reserve or Natural Monument category. It is very popular as a protected plant. For example,

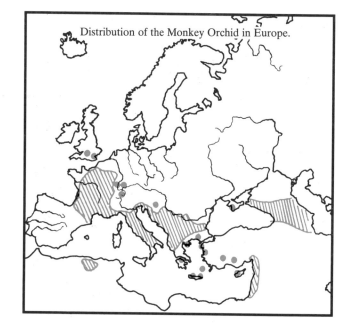

Distribution of the Monkey Orchid in Europe.

it is one of several protected species most often depicted on postage stamps.

This, the most beautiful among the British orchids, was formerly widespread in woodland on limestone in Derbyshire, Yorkshire, Durham and Cumbria and in areas of the northern Pennines. Now it survives in only one location in northern England. The virtual extinction of the Lady's Slipper in Britain is being ascribed to years of uprooting and picking by gardeners and botanists. Now the only remaining area of occurrence is protected by a Site of Special Scientific Interest. The British Red Data Book species is moreover covered by phase 1 of the English Nature's Species Recovery Programme aimed at increasing populations of plants and animals that are under threat.

Another exotic orchid found in Europe is the **Violet Bird's Nest Orchid** (*Limodorum abortivum* (L.) Sw.). This perennial orchid with a thick and short ground rhizome and numerous tuberously intertwined roots is conspicuous at first sight in that it does not have green leaves. The flower-bearing stem is usually about 0.5 m sometimes almost 1 m high, and is steel blue to greyish violet in colour. The leaves are developed as many sheathing scales of a brownish colour. The lax inflorescence is formed by 5 to 20 conspicuous, large (4—5 cm in diameter) light bluish violet, dark veined flowers which bloom from the end of May to July. The seeds measuring about 1.5 mm in length, are the largest of all European wild orchids. The germination and development of this plant are incredibly complicated because of its way of life in co-existence with fungi.

The scientific species name appears to indicate that the herb contains substances with abortive effects. This is not true but formerly the Violet Bird's Nest Orchid was gathered for this purpose and used in folk medicine. It could be that the name is actually derived from the imperfect appearance of the plant without the green leaves and often almost closed up flowers. In France and Germany, at the beginning of the century, cases were observed and described of the plants flowering and bearing fruits under the soil surface. The rhizome of the *Limodorum* is set over 1 m deep in the ground and therefore it is very difficult for the plant to penetrate the soil, especially in years of drought. This is evidently also one of the reasons why the Violet Bird's Nest Orchid appears rather irregularly in its well known localities. In some years it is not seen at all.

The typical Mediterranean range of the Violet Bird's Nest Orchid includes Asia Minor and North Africa. This orchid occurs in great abundance in dwarf juniper oak woodland on the south Crimean coast. The western border of its range runs through France to Belgium and Luxembourg. Central Europe is on the very edge of the range with very rare sparse occurrences in Switzerland, Germany (particularly Eifel, the Mosel Valley, Kaiserstuhl), in Austria, Hungary and the Czech and Slovak Republics (very rarely and irregularly in southern Moravia and in the southern half of Slovakia). In all these countries the species is protected by law. Of course the most effective protection of the plant lies in the essential careful maintenance of its biotopes. These are above all thermophilous oak woods where it grows on alkaline humous ground.

Another wonderful woodland orchid, which grows in similar habitats, is a representative of the most numerous western and central European orchid genus — the **Lady Orchid** (*Orchis purpurea* Huds.). Of all central and western European species of the genus, it is the most conspicuous, most robust and, without a doubt, the most beautiful. When in flower, it grows to a height of 30 to 80 cm. The large (up to over 15 cm long), pale to dark green, obovate leaves which have a slight shine on the upper side are densely clustered in the lowest part of the stem, thus giving the impression of a ground leaf rosette. The broadly cylindrical inflorescence is up to 30 cm long, consisting of numerous, usually dense, quite large (about 3 cm in diameter) flowers. These flowers have a broad three-lobed whitish or light red, darker dotted lip and dark purple perianth segments with an even dark pattern, converging into a short helmet. In central and western Europe the Lady Orchid flowers in May and June. It is quite a variable species espe-

123

cially with regard to its flowers and also creates interesting hybrids with other species of its genus.

The Lady Orchid is a sub-Mediterranean species. It grows from northern Spain across to the Transcaucasus; it can be found in England, Denmark, southern Scandinavia and the Baltic states. It also grows in North Africa, the Crimea, on the Black Sea coast of Caucasus, and in the south-east it penetrates Turkey. The centre of its range however is central Europe where the Lady Orchid grows in hills and highlands (up to 700 m above sea level, in southern Germany only, north of the Danube) in calcareous rich decomposed humous soil and in warm regions. It is found in open woodland or in scrub, sometimes also  in grasslands of a steppe character. In most European countries it is protected by law, including England. Formerly more widespread, the current occurrence of the Lady Orchid in Britain is confined mainly to Kent.

As regards conservation status, the same situation exists with another wonderful European orchid. This is the shorter (up to 0.5 m), also robust, pale yellow flowering **Pale-flowered Orchid** (*Orchis pallens* L.). It is somewhat less thermophilous and flowers earlier — from April to May. It also appears in beech woods, in mountain meadows and higher altitudes (up to about 1,500 m above sea level). In central Europe, on the northern border of its range, it grows most abundantly in the Slovak Carpa-

thians. In western Europe it grows only in France.

The European orchids are interesting because of their anthropomorphic flowers (i.e. resembling a human figure or animal primate) and this is particularly obvious in the case of the rare **Monkey Orchid** (*Orchis simia* Lam.). It is a perennial, 20 to 40 cm high herb with inflorescences which are more orbicular than cylindrical, dense pinkish red flowers and a three-lobed lip resembling the figure of a small monkey. It flowers in April and May.

The Monkey Orchid is a Mediterranean species. Its range includes the Crimea, the Caucasus, an extensive area of Asia Minor and North Africa. Certain sub-Atlantic tendencies are shown in its occurrences in England. It is found in central Europe, in the west to Switzerland and western Germany (the Saar, the Rhineland), and in the east to Hungary. It is strictly protected on those border regions. It is a thermophilous and calciphilous plant. It grows on sites in full sunlight and in semi-shade in open woodland and scrub at their margins, in glades and dry grassland.

Base-rich grassland is also the main habitat of the Monkey Orchid in Britain, where the species is included in the British Red Data Book. Many colonies have been destroyed by removal and burning of turf, uprooting, rabbit grazing and ploughing. The Monkey Orchid is a protected species in England, moreover four of its remaining sites are covered by protected areas of various categories. Formerly more widespread, it is now confined to five locations in Kent, Oxfordshire and Yorkshire. One of them was created by a transplant to preserve the species.

We have already mentioned one of the most common European wild lilies. The other lily is usually a woodland plant species, the **Martagon Lily** (*Lilium martagon* L.). It is a very robust perennial. Erect, unbranched stems carrying leaves at the bottom part only emerge annually from a folded, yellow underground bulb. The middle elongated leaves are set in whorls on the stem. The stem ends in an inflo-

rescence with 2 to 40 large flowers with six reddish purple spotted sepals, which are 3 to 3.5 cm long and folded back recurved (hence the German species name Turkenbund — Turk's cap). It flowers from June to August, the season varying with altitude and climate.

The Martagon Lily is a highly ornamental plant, often cultivated in gardens for decoration in various varieties. It is one of the plants with the largest flowers in native European flora, which is why some plant-growers try to acquire it from the wild. Also picking flowers for bouquets leads to a decline in the natural populations.

The Martagon Lily is a Eurasian species. The north-western border of its range runs through central Europe. It is found in deciduous woods from lowlands right up into mountain meadows, in the mountains in the dwarf pine belt and in sub-Alpine meadows right up to about 2,500 m above sea level. In higher mountain areas it has more intensive, richer coloured and larger flowers. It is protected by law in Switzerland, Germany, Austria, the Czech Republic, Slovakia and Poland.

The Martagon Lily can also be found in Britain with scattered sites in woods and scrub in England and Wales as far north as Cumbria. It belongs to those British plants whose status as native or introduced species is particularly obscure. Probably in some parts of Britain the Martagon Lily may be indigenous, but elsewhere it has spread freely from gardens in which it has been grown at least since the early Middle Ages.

An interesting but so far little researched woodland species, similar to bellflowers and their relatives, is the **Adenophora** (*Adenophora liliifolia* (L.) Bess.) of the Bellflower family (*Campanulaceae*). It is a hairless perennial, to 1 m high, with an erect,

densely leafed stem branched when in flower. The bottom leaves are long, petiole, heart-shaped and toothed along the edges, and these die when the plant is in flower. The upper leaves are smaller, with short stalks or even sessile. The funnel-shaped campanulate flowers, with a whitish to blue corolla up to 2 cm in length from which a style with three stigmas emerge, compose relatively rich although rather lax racemes or branched panicles. The flowers bloom from the end of July to the beginning of October.

The Adenophora is a European/western Siberian sub-continental species with certain Mediterranean trends in its geographical distribution. What is interesting is that it grows in central Europe even though very rarely in various biotopes. In Switzerland it grows on only one site in southern Tessin (the famous locality of Monte San Giorgio) in thermophilous grassland with numerous Mediterranean species. In the whole of the western part of Germany the only regions where the Adenophora can be found are the warm and fertile, temporarily damp meadows and bushes at the confluence of Isar and Danube rivers not far from Deggendorf (it is listed as in danger of extinction and a protected species). It also grows in Austria mainly in the boggy meadows (it is even listed as a characteristic species of plants of the phyto-sociological union of the Purple Moorgrass (*Molinion*) in the southern part of the Vienna basin. It is found rarely growing in Bohemia and Moravia, in woods and glades, sometimes surprisingly in managed forests. In recent years its existence in a number of formerly recorded sites has not been confirmed. It does not grow in the east of Germany, but is found in various places in woods and meadows of Poland. It is more abundant in Slovakia where it grows in thermophilous oak woods or in scrub and steppes which have replaced woodland, but also in

open deciduous, mixed and coniferous woods and in their glades and clearings from hills to lower and medium levels of the Carpathian mountain ranges. It quite often appears in Hungary where it can be found mainly in alluvial forests with a predominance of elm and ash trees in positions out of reach of regular floods (the so-called Pannonian hard riverine wood).

Primroses are the main genus of the Primrose family (*Primulaceae*). As yet in Europe these woodland species are not too rare, but definitely deserve attention from the point of view of nature conservation. The woodland species have yellow flowers. The **Cowslip** (*Primula veris* L.) has flowers of an egg yolk colour. It is a variable species and is represented in Europe by several subspecies. The Cowslip is a perennial with a short and strong rhizome and numerous thin roots in the ground. The rhizome issues forth a ground rosette of tough ovate to elongated ovate, crenate leaves with protruding nerves. When young the leaves have revolute margins. The scape is 10 to 25 (rarely more) cm long and terminates in an umbel of pleasantly scanted flowers. The flowers have tubular inflated greenish calyxes and long tubular, dark yellow corollas which are funnel-shaped at the mouth, with orange markings inside. The name of the *Primula* genus (Latin: *primus* = first) relates to the fact that the flower blossoms early in April and at the beginning of May. The German name 'Schlüsselblume' (key flower) came about from the more or less one-sided umbel of flowers resembling the teeth of a key.

The leaves of the Cowslip contain a lot of vitamin C, but are inedible because the plant also contains saponins. The saponin content, which encourages the formation of red blood cells, is greatest during the period of flowering and then in the autumn (in some years primroses flower for a second time in the autumn). The Cowslip is an ancient effective medicinal plant. Apart from the rhizome, the flower is also picked — either all of it or just the yellow corolla. It must be quickly and carefully dried in the shade at a low temperature. The essential oil and glycosides contained in the flowers clears phlegm and relieves coughs. The drug made from the Cowslip forms a part of many medicines, especially teas recom-

126

Distribution of the Dwarf Cherry in Europe.

mended for lung and respiratory illnesses and bron-chitis. In some European countries — e.g. in England — primrose wine used to be made from the Cowslip flowers in the rural areas.

The Cowslip is a European/western Siberian species. In the west it also grows in the British Isles, where it is widespread in much of England, southern and central Scotland and central Ireland, scarce else-where. In the north it can be found in a narrow strip along the Baltic coast and sporadically in the south-ern part of Scandinavia. It is protected by law in Ger-many, Poland, Austria and the Czech Republic. The basic biotope of the Cowslip in Europe is deciduous woodland in lowlands and hills. It is a characteristic species of oak woods. In the mountains — in the Alps and Carpathians — it appears in meadows up to over 1,500 m above sea level. In the lowlands and hills it is also found in substitute secondary habitats such as drier meadows, sometimes also meadow steppes, cultured meadows and turfs or pastures because it was forced out of many forests due to the change in the forest tree composition. However, plants grow-ing close to gardens, may have spread from gardens and these can be recognized by the different colours of the flowers. Cowslip is cultivated in garden va-rieties with flowers of diverse colour from orange to red violet. The Cowslip has appeared on several European red lists as a species in low threat categories.

In many towns of central Europe, bunches of primrose scapes with flowers are sold in florist shops in spring. More common than the species described above, this is the **Oxlip** (*Primula elatior* (L.) Hill). It differs from the Cowslip by its calyx pressed against the corolla tube and by the pale yellow corolla with the limb broad and flat. Sometimes it flowers earlier than the Cowslip (later in the mountains). It is

a European species with a sub-Atlantic tendency and therefore does not grow far into eastern Europe. Apart from isolated occurrences (relatively abun-dant in Rügen) it does not occur in the northern cen-tral European lowlands. In the mountains it is found up to over 2,000 m above sea level. It grows in fresh and cooler deciduous woods of various compositions of alder, maple, ash and beech (*Fagetalia*). It also grows naturally in meadows, mainly mountain ones. Cultivated meadows have often provided it with suitable substitute habitats. It is a plant of fertile clay, fresh to wet soils. It also has medicinal qualities. It is protected by law in Germany, Poland, Hungary, Austria and in the Czech Republic.

In Britain, the Oxlip is restricted to some eastern counties of England, where it is common locally, es-pecially in ancient coppice woodland.

It is the **Primrose** (*Primula vulgaris* Huds. = *acaulis* (L.) Hill.) which in central Europe is classed in the highest threat categories on lists of protected species, but it is common in western Europe includ-ing Britain. As its species name indicates, yellow un-scented flowers grow on short stalks directly from the centre of the leafy rosette. The plant is therefore only 5 to 10 cm high. It flowers very early from March on-wards. In appearance it resembles the low primroses cultivated a lot for decoration in flower-pots, in gar-dens, municipal parks, in cemeteries, etc. Dozens of varieties of different colours have been derived from the wild Primrose as the original genetic resource.

The Primrose is a species with an interesting At-lantic-Mediterranean distribution. Its range stret-ches through western Europe from Portugal and Spain across the British Isles to Denmark and along the coast of western Norway. It continues into north Africa, Italy, the Balkans, Black Sea region and the Caucasus. So most of central Europe is an empty

127

The Dwarf Cherry in fully blossom in May.

space in its range. It is only more frequent in Switzerland, in the southern part of Germany, Austria (mainly in the Alpine foothills and the Alps where it grows to about 1,000 m above sea level) and in Hungary from where a promontory of continuous range extends north to Slovakia. It does not grow in the Czech Republic or in the east of Germany. In Poland there are several scattered sites in the northern lowlands particularly close to the Baltic coast. It is a characteristic species of deciduous woodland and scrub, also growing in natural and culture grasslands. It requires fertile soil and, being an Atlantic species, mild winters.

Although the Primrose is the most common species of its genus and is widespread throughout Britain, it deserves attention from the point of view of nature conservation. It is currently diminishing rapidly in some counties due to modern agricultural practices and over-collecting, in spite of the fact that the plant is tolerant to grazing and trampling. In Britain, its hybrid with the Oxlip (called False Oxlip) is common in the wild, where the two parent species meet. Also a form of Primrose with pink flowers is sometimes found near gardens: this hybrid is explained by botanists as a result of a long-range cross-pollination with garden flowers.

In view of their many different properties which are useful to man, European yellow flowering wild woodland primroses represent a very valuable plant genetic resource. If we also add the aesthetic, recreational and inspiring contribution of their flowering colonies in early spring in the open countryside and in settlement, it would be a pity if this wealth were to vanish.

Scrubs and hedgerows in Europe create a number of interesting plant communities and have become significant biotopes for the preservation of plant genetic resources. The plant associations of this type are included in the plant communities order *Prunetalia* named after several representatives of the Cherries and Plums (genus *Prunus*) of the Rose family (*Rosaceae*). This is so in the case of the **Blackthorn** (*Prunus spinosa* L.), the **St Lucie's Cherry** (*Prunus mahaleb* L.) and the **Dwarf** or **Sour Cherry** (*Prunus fructicosa* Pall.), whose own union of plant associations, *Prunion fructicosae*, is particularly typical of rocky and stony hillside, especially on limestone and loess in eastern and south-eastern Europe.

The Dwarf Cherry is a shrub 1 m high with thornless and hairless twigs. It has elliptical, elongated obovate, 3—4 cm long, tough, glossy crenate leaves. There are 2 to 5 pure white flowers growing in umbels on shortened lateral twigs. During flowering — at the end of April and beginning of May — the shrub is covered with these flowers. Later the flowers develop into edible and tasty drupes measuring up to 1 cm in diameter — bright red to dark red cherries.

As a close relative of cultivated cherries, the Dwarf Cherry is very important for the selection of fruit trees. It is also cultivated as an ornamental plant. Wild sites are natural gene banks of this important genetic resource. It is a European/western Siberian species which is rare in central Europe, the western border of its range. The Dwarf Cherry is on central European red lists and its areas of occurrence are part of the motivation for establishing protected territories. It deserves greater attention in active nature conservation on stony and rocky steep hillsides, but only in the warmest and driest regions.

BEECH WOODS, HIGHLAND AND MOUNTAIN FORESTS, PINE AND SPRUCE WOODLANDS, THE DWARF PINE BELT

The border of a mountain beech wood: the Beech (*Fagus sylvatica*) is the most widespread of native deciduous trees in central and western European woodlands. Beech woods are very diverse.

The most widespread native tree of western and central European woodland is the **Beech** (*Fagus sylvatica* L.). In south-eastern Europe it is replaced by the Eastern Beech (*Fagus orientalis* Lipsky). The Beech and the beech woods occur from central Europe south-west into the Pyrenees, west into south-east England, the Midlands and south Wales, and north to Denmark and southern Sweden. In the east they follow through the Carpathians to Romania, they occur in the Balkan mountains, in northern, central and southern Italy, and can also be found in Corsica and Sicily. The predominance of beech in natural vegetation is also expressed in the name of the plant sociological order of European deciduous forests — *Fagetalia*. This unit also includes deciduous woods which we dealt with in the preceding chapter. The actual beech woods belong to the *Fagion* union.

Central and western European beech woods are very diverse within the scope of their union. The number of differentiated and described plant associations is extraordinarily high and some of them, for example beech woods with yew trees (*Taxo-Fagetum*), appear on the red lists of European plant communities. The above-mentioned association belongs to a group of rather dry beech woods, growing locally on calcareous ground, in Hercynian hills and highlands as well as in the foothills of the Alps, Pyrenees, and Carpathians. Fresh calciphilous beech woods and beech woods growing on European brown soils are developed like typical calciphilous beech woods on limestone and similar ground in hills and lower highlands or like Melick (*Melica*) beech woods growing on moraine humps in northern Germany and Poland. These communities have always had a relatively well developed herb canopy of diverse species structure. Substantially poorer in species are beech woods growing on acid humus with woodrushes (*Luzula*) and Bilberry (*Vaccinium*).

The altitude conditions the original natural vegetation of Europe in the form of fir-beech woodlands, mountain mixed woods of beech and some other deciduous trees with firs and spruces at e.g. between 500—900 m above sea level in the Sudeten mountains, 400—1,200 m above sea level in the Bohemian and Bavarian Forests, 500—900 m above sea level in the Black Forest (Schwarzwald) and 600—1,000 m above sea level in the Swabian Jura mountains (Schwäbische Alb). This belt also includes important central European virgin forest reserves which open up the first pages of the history of nature conservation on the European continent and the world as a whole. In 1838 one 'enlightened' estate owner declared the protection of two virgin forest patches in the Novohradské Mountains in southern Bohemia. In 1858 at the initiative of the forest personnel, Duke Schwarzenberg gave up the management of the Boubínský (Kubany) Virgin Forest in the Šumava (Bohemian Forest). This virgin forest became an open-air woodland research laboratory for study of the development of woodland. Its hundred year tradition is unique in the world. Its counterparts across the frontier in Bavaria for example are the Mittelsteighütte am Zwiesler Waldhaus Reserve or the Rachel Reserve in the Bavarian Forest. The Swiss have their own famous Alpine virgin forest reserve (Derborence in Valais) and the Austrians have the prominent Rothwald Virgin Reserve in the lower Austrian foothills of the Alps. The further east, the more vital are the remnants of the virgin forest in the Carpathians, culminating in one of the most eastern points of central Europe — in the trilaterally protected area of Stužica on the frontier between Slovakia, Poland and the Ukraine, now a core zone of a trilateral Biosphere Reserve under preparation.

Today the virgin forest reserves represent rare islands of ecological balance and diversity. They are laboratories for scientific reseach and long-term monitoring of the state and change of the environment, as well as excellent natural history and ecological open air classrooms in the heart of nature. Their management is becoming ever more complicated and demanding because of the increasingly harsh local and global external influences ranging from the growth in tourism to air pollution.

Of the original natural beech woods in central and northwest Europe, only fragments remain which have not been transformed into uniform areas of coniferous trees particularly the spruce. The former extensive beech woods in the Ore Mountains, the Iser Mountains and the Giant Mountains in the Czech Republic have been replaced by commercial spruce forests, the flora has changed as many species growing in natural beech woods have become a rarity. It only needed several post war decades of intensive development in industry and energy using sulphuric lignite as fuel to transform those sites into dying or altogether lifeless tree skeletons, into horrible tree cemeteries. What is going to happen? In place of the former forests there are expanding mountain grass prairies of Hairy Small-reed (*Calamagrostis villosa*), of the woody plants only the rowan and the birch are surviving in the most exposed areas, the species diversity is declining.

However, dying forests can also be observed in other regions of central and north-western Europe.

The natural spruce woods here were far more restricted than today's mixed forests. They occurred above all in the mountain belt of the Carpathians and Alps, but also at higher altitudes of certain lower European mountain ranges, and more rarely on the borders of peat-bogs even in Quaternary northern lowlands or on the bottom of deep and damp rock gorges, for example in the Elbe Highlands, and 'Bohemia-Saxony-Switzerland'. Such growths differ distinctly from artificial monocultures in their structure and obviously in the herb canopy hosting many remarkable plant species.

Also the Scots Pine, extending in central and north-west Europe to approximately the southwestern border of its range, used to be much more scarce before forest managment made it the most common forest tree. The remnants of natural European pine woods often provide important biotopes for the survival of many plant species, and today definitely require special territorial protection whether this concerns pine woods with the Spring Heath (*Erica carnea*, syn. *E. herbacea*) in the northern Alps, acid pine wood on the poor sands of Quaternary lowlands in northern central Europe or sparse pine woods on sand dunes representing the final stage of their natural colonization by vegetation, or pine woods on the margins of raised peat-bogs and drier forest peat-bogs. In many of these pine woods even the dominating species, the **Scots Pine** (*Pinus silvestris* L.), deserves careful conservation even though it appears to be quite common. To be more precise, certain of its local ecotypes valued for their excellent properties in building require careful conservation. For example,

Distribution of the Silver Fir in Europe.

The interior of a central European middle mountain mixed virgin forest; one of the oldest nature reserve in Europe, the Boubínský (Kubany) Virgin Forest in the Bohemian Forest, Czech Republic.

The Silver Fir (*Abies alba*) is dying out in European forests — from the west to the east. The fir cones, growing erect on the top branches like candles, do not fall but disintegrate on the tree.

there are Bohemian Pines the 'Třeboň Pine' of southern Bohemia and the 'Jetřichovice Pine' of Bohemia-Saxony-Switzerland. This significant genetic resource was one of the reasons why the Třeboň area was declared a Biosphere Reserve within the international UNESCO 'Man and the Biosphere' Programme, and why the Elbe Sandstones are also in the process of being upgraded to a bilateral transboundary National Park.

Above the mountain tree limit there are usually thick growths of the Mountain Pine (*Pinus mugo* Turra) vegetation belt.

In parts of southern Britain the Scots Pine has been established for many centuries on heathy soils, though it was probably not natural in the first instance. It commonly grows together with birches on soils of low or moderate nutrient status. A remarkable woodland region is the great Caledonian Forest in the Scottish Highlands. This is a dark and rather sombre forest of the boreal regions — of the type generally called taiga, with a rich assortment of herbs, ferns, mosses, lichens and fungi. The Scottish Caledonian forests are far more restricted now than previously and are in need of careful conservation: many of the remaining woods actually are established nature reserves now.

Foresters, naturalists, conservationists and all nature lovers are sad to see that in central and western European forests their most beautiful coniferous tree is declining. This tree, called the Virgin by poets, is the graceful, delicate **Silver Fir** (*Abies alba* Mill.). What is the cause of its decline? The opinions are not altogether unanimous. It was thought that the cause was the same disease as that killing elms, or that the fir is an evolutionary type which has not proved vital enough, and is therefore naturally declining. Nevertheless, everyone agrees that air pollution is a substantial cause. Today it is clear that pollutants in the air are seriously damaging and that fir forests and perhaps the Silver Fir as a species are in danger of extinction. In south-eastern Poland the Swietokrzyskie Mountain National Park on Lysa Gora (Bald Mountain) and the area of the north-eastern Malopolskie highland was until recently renowned for its healthy fir-beech woods. With industrial development in the nearby city of Kielce and its environs from which the predominating west winds

blow towards Lysa Gora, the tops of fir trees began to dry up and today entire trees are dying. The fir-beech wood ecosystem is beginning to collapse. In the Czech Republic and eastern Germany the Silver Fir is classified on the red list as a threatened plant species.

The Silver Fir grows to a height of 65 metres. It has an upright cylindrical trunk with whitish grey smooth bark which later changes into brownish grey scales. At first the growth of this conifer is conical and very regular, later its shape becomes cylindrical and old firs are conspicuous for their flat crown in the shape of a stork nest. When young the branches grow in regular whorls and later they protrude from the trunk at right angles. The linear flat needles, glossy deep green above and with two white stripes beneath, are usually laid out on the branch into two rows. The cones stand erect on the twigs like candles and can never be found under firs as they disintegrate on the tree and their peg-like projections last for several more years after the scales fall off with the seeds.

From the economic point of view it is desirable to maintain the Silver Fir in the woods. It is a very productive tree, resistant to winds, it can withstand shade and does not diminsh the quality of the soil as much as the spruce. Its timber is used in the building industry (especially for water constructions due to its considerable endurance in water), in the furniture industry and for wood carving.

The Silver Fir is relatively demanding with regard to soil and habitat moisture. It suffers from frost and above all from animals because today most forests in Europe, due to the great popularity of hunting, are inhabited by game populations, exceeding their carrying capacity. The Silver Fir is also a beautiful, decorative tree, but because of its demands and vulnerability, in particular its sensivity towards air pollution, certain exotic firs, mainly north American species,

are cultivated in our gardens and parks. The young specimens of Silver Fir, in view of their regular flat branches with deep green needles, make ideal Christmas trees. However, due to its decline and the careful conservation of regenerating trees, the Silver Fir has almost completely disappeared from the European Christmas markets (in Switzerland the Silver Fir was still quite frequently sold in the 1970s).

The range of the Silver Fir is restricted to central Europe and certain southern mountain ranges: the Pyrenees, the Corsican mountains, the Apennines, the Abruzzo plateau, the Calabrian mountains, the Balkan mountains down to northern Greece. From the Carpathians the Silver Fir extends far down into Romania. There are isolated range isles in the French Massif Central and in Normandy. The central European north-western border of its range runs from the Vosges through southern Westphalia to the Harz, through Thuringia to Saxony and Lusatia and across central Poland (its most northern point reaching up to Warsaw and there is an islet further northeast between the rivers Warta and Niemen). The Silver Fir is not found in the Hungarian lowland.

This foothill and mountain conifer, more rare in lower hills, mainly grows from 400 to 900 metres above sea level. In the Alps and Pyrenees it grows up to almost 2,000 m above sea level, in the Carpathians to about 1,300 m. It requires fertile and damp soil. The tree grows in mixed woods with the beech and spruce, the remains of which are protected today in nature reserves. The Silver Fir is still in good condition in eastern Europe, but there are fears as to whether the damaging influence of man's industrial activities will also cause it to disappear from these regions. It rarely naturally composes more or less pure stands. Such virgin forests have survived, are protected and accessible (by nature trail) at the Rozto-

czanski National Park in the Lublin highlands of south-eastern Poland. In Britain the Silver Fir is fairly widely planted.

A deciduous shrub of European deciduous and mixed woods and forests is the **Mezereon** (*Daphne mezereum* L.) of the Daphne family (*Thymelaeaceae*), which is represented in Europe only by a few genera. This shrub with hairy young shoots grows to a height of 50 cm — 1 m, rarely more. It has very tough, unbreakable timber. Conspicuous sparse clusters of deep pinkish purple, heavily scented four-part flowers growing from 0.5 to 1 cm in length, develop on the bare branches before the leaves appear. The Mezereon flowers from the end of January (in the warmest lowland areas) to May — June (high in the mountains). After flowering, oblong, short stalked, alternate leaves grow which are conspicuously crowded towards the shoot tips. Orbicular bright, shiny, red berries develop from the flowers. The entire plant it poisonous because it contains the substance mezerin.

The Mezereon is a European/western Siberian sub-continental species widespread almost all over Europe and penetrating deeply into Asia. It grows in fertile, particularly calcareous soils with a rich humus content, in shade or semi-shade, from lowland (where it is more rare) to mountains (in the Alps to over 2,000 m above sea level) individually or in great colonies. It is a characteristic species of the European high-rank deciduous forests — *Fagetalia*. It rarely grows in the central European northern lowlands, and is abundant in beech woods along the Baltic Sea coast.

In Britain it is localized and rare from Sussex to Yorkshire in woods, scrub and also pastures on calcareous soils, sometimes also occurring as a garden escape.

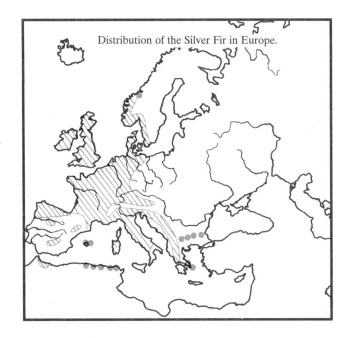

Distribution of the Silver Fir in Europe.

◁ ◁ The Mezereon (*Daphne mezereum*), widespread in various types of forest from the lowlands to the mountains, flowers as early as the end of winter before the leaves develop.

◁ The Holly (*Ilex aquifolium*), a shrub or small tree of shady undergrowth in damp beech woods, lives for almost three hundred years. In the winter its dark green, prickly pointed leaves do not fall but have an attractive shine.

It is protected by law in most European countries including the UK. It is not found on the German red list. It would appear that it is quite common in central Europe although nowhere in great abundance. In early spring its flowers attract unwanted attention. In Bohemia along the Sázava river a Mezereon site is protected by the state. Several hundred bushes are found there, but despite the statute of territorial protection, these never grow to more than 0.5 m because people constantly cut them or break the flowering branches. To most people the mere sight of this shrub's exceptionally natural beauty does not suffice. The Mezereon is popularly cultivated in gardens, often in the white-flowering form, for its decorative appearance — both in flower and fruit. For centuries it was cultivated in country gardens and curative properties were ascribed to it. It was used as an emetic and laxative, to treat rheumatism and gout and externally for the treatment of skin rashes. In Germany it was used in folk veterinary medicine to treat parasitic worms in horses. Most individual plants cultivated in gardens originated from the wild. Today the Mezereon can be purchased relatively easily at expert gardening firms. Many sites have disappeared as a consequence of commercial forest management and particularly as a result of the changes in forest composition.

The evergreen **Spurge Laurel** (*Daphne laureola* L.) with greenish yellow flowers is a sub-Mediterranean species with an oceanic tendency. It is widespread in England, scarce in Wales and absent or alien in Scotland and Ireland. A characteristic species of Alpine heath pine woods is the pink flowering *Daphne striata* Tratt. which greatly resembles the *Daphne cneorum* L. in appearance.

Of an altogether different appearance, place in the plant system and distribution in Europe is the **Holly** (*Ilex aquifolium* L.). It is the sole European representative of the Holly family (*Aquifoliaceae*) and its prominent Holly (*Ilex*) genus. The Holly provides precious refined wood for carving, furniture making, etc. The popular Paraguayan tea is made from the leaves of the South American species of holly. The branches with tough prickly tipped, shiny dark green leaves and round red berries are a popular Christmas symbol in England, and also more and more often in central Europe. The Holly is also cultivated for decoration in gardens and parks.

The Holly is an evergreen shrub or small tree with hairless branches except for the young shoots. It grows to a height of 10 m and lives for 300 years. The leathery leaves are ovate and up to 8 cm long. The tiny whitish flowers bloom in May and June. The bright red fruits stay on the branches for a long time until autumn or winter providing food for birds which thus propagate the plant.

This remarkable species of European flora occupies a distinct Atlantic-Mediterranean range. It grows from south-western Norway across western Europe (including the British Isles) and Italy right up to the border of North Africa. The eastern border of its range runs through central Europe. It extends from Rügen across the southern border of the Harz towards the Rhine, Alpine foothills and the lower altitudes of the Alps reaching Bavaria and sporadically right over to Austria. The Holly grows in medium fertile, neutral to slightly acid, often sandy soils in areas with temperate winter, in sun or shade, most frequently in the undergrowth of deciduous and mixed forests, particularly in beech woods. It is protected by law in Switzerland, Austria and Germany.

In Britain, the Holly is widespread except in the extreme north and absent from most of the smaller islands. Though abundant in woods, hedges and in the sites of former woodland, it has a special significance for conservationists: it is an indicator of woodland antiquity. Also individual holly trees may themselves be very long-lived, such as the notable group in Shropshire on Lord's Hill, above Snailbeach. The holly trees there have a girth of more than 1.5 m and are well over 200 years old. In Britain Holly is a traditional hedgerow plant, and it was formerly encouraged near smallholdings as it was economically valuable as winter fodder. Hollies can be devastated by hard winters, but the Holly is by no

◁ The Common Wintergreen (*Pyrola minor*) has a basal rosette of stalked, heart-shaped leaves resembling a pear tree leaf: when in flower, the style does not protrude from the white or pinkish globose corolla.

▽ The Umbellate Wintergreen (*Chimaphila umbellata*) is dying out in Europe; it also has highly decorative shiny, leathery leaves grouped together at the ends of the shoots. This plant, living in a complicated symbiosis with fungi, is a rare inhabitant of mossy pine woods.

The Ghost Orchid (*Epipogium aphyllum*) is one of the ▷ wild European orchids without any chlorophyll: it grows very rarely in humous damp soils in the shade of woods from uplands to mountains.

The Lesser Twayblade (*Listera cordata*), a small orchid ▷ ▽ of the European north and mountains, can be recognized easily by the pair of two opposite almost sessile leaves at the lower third of the stem.

means threatened in Britain, as it is in central Europe.

As indicated by their name, plants of the Wintergreen family (*Pyrolaceae*) are also evergreen. In Europe this family includes perennial herbs with 4—5 part flowers and with hibernating, green, alternate and simple leaves. Up until recently, these herbs were no rarity in European forests, above all in coniferous forests, and particularly in pine woods. However in recent years they have started to occur less and less frequently. It is often the case that they cannot be found for several years even on a known site, where no apparent damage could have occurred, for example to the structure of the forest growth.

The Wintergreens have a more complicated way of nourishment than any other green plant. In a similar way to orchids, they live in a symbiosis with fungi in the form of nutrition called mycotrophy. The still relatively little explored fungi are substantially sensitive towards certain heterogeneous impacts and substances. So without any direct destruction of a habitat or felling of forest trees the populations can be damaged by air pollution even from a distant source, the chemical spraying of the forest against pests or the application of fertilizers. The protection of such species is a tough job even for experts. Mycotrophy makes it difficult to cultivate these plants in protective cultures, to transplant them to substitute habitats or, vice versa, from a culture to the open countryside.

Perhaps the prettiest of all Wintergreens (and today the rarest in Europe) is the **Umbellate Wintergreen** (*Chimaphila umbellata* (L.) Bart.). It is directly in danger of extinction today in Germany and the Czech Republic. It is a sub-shrub up to 25 cm high with leathery, ovate leaves grouped at the tops of the final shoots. The flowers with white or pinkish

petals and red anthers measuring over 1 cm in diameter, grow in corymbs, 2 to 7, at the end of stems. They appear from June to August.

The Umbellate Wintergreen in a Eurasian-continental circumpolar (also occurring in North America) species. The western border of its range in Europe runs from southern Sweden and Norway to the German Baltic coast, down the Elbe and from the Elbe towards the upper Rhine. From here the southern border moves eastwards, up in a fold reaching Bavaria and Austria northwards from the Danube and continues along the northern Slovak border, with isolated occurrences further south to Slova-

kia and Hungary. It is not native in Britain. The Umbellate Wintergreen grows mainly in moderately damp, mossy and humous semi-shaded pine woods on sandy, often rather calcareous soils. More often it occurs in the lowlands of northern Germany and Poland. A secondary spread of the forest pine culture once also contributed to the more widespread occurrence of Umbellate Wintergreen. However, the influence of today's civilization has a destructive effect on the plant. In Germany it was once used in folk medicine. The leaves contain the glycosides arbutin and ursone. In central Bohemia the ornamental twigs were used for All Souls' Day bouquets and wreaths. The plant is protected by law in several European countries.

Representatives of the actual *Pyrola* genus are protected wherever they are especially rare. In the Hungarian lowland they are protected by law (4 species altogether) and territorially (particularly the remarkable relict pine virgin forest at Fenyöfö on the north-western slopes of the Bakony Forest). The *Pyrola* species are found in abundance in the pine woods of the northern central European lowlands, particularly in Germany and Poland; they are also characteristic plants of the Scottish pine woods.

The **Common Wintergreen** (*Pyrola minor* L.) has stalked ovate leaves in a ground rosette from which 5 to 20 cm high flower-bearing stems grow with 4 to 16 orbicularly closed, nodding white flowers within a multilateral raceme. In Britain it is localised and declining. The **Intermediate Wintergreen** (*Pyrola media* Sw.) is most often found on central European red lists in the highest threat categories. It is also rare and declining in Britain, where it occurs mostly in Scotland and Northern Ireland. It is similar to the previous species, but differs from it in its style protruding from an enclosed corolla.

The non-green **Ghost Orchid** (*Epipogium aphyllum* Sw.) belongs to the rare plants of European beech woods and coniferous mountain forests. The English name is derived from its translucent, pale, whitish, yellowish or pinkish appearance. It is a perennial with an underground coral-like rhizome. Underground protuberances grow from the rhizome and these form new rhizomes. The biology of this distinctly mycotrophic (completely dependent on the symbiosis with fungi) species is very complicated. It can happen that none of the plants at a well-known, undamaged site flower for a number of years before the prerequisites are re-created in the underground organs for the growth of flower-bearing stems. The stems are 10 to 20 cm high, erect, hairless, translucent with lax inflorescence of 2 to 5, exceptionally even 8 pale yellow flowers measuring up to 3 cm in diameter with the lip pointing upwards. The plant flowers from June to August.

The Ghost Orchid occurs in Euro-Siberian and eastern Asian deciduous woods. In Europe it is scarce, mostly rare, from the Pyrenees almost as far

as the Artic Circle, from England to the European part of the former USSR. It grows in oak and beech woods, mixed forests and spruce woods from hills to lower mountain altitudes; in the Alps and Carpathians it climbs to an altitude of about 1,500 m above sea level. It grows in humous, shaded and damp habitats, most often near the sources of forest brooks. It is protected by law in Switzerland, Germany, Austria, the Czech Republic, Hungary, and also in the UK. In Britain it is extinct in Herefordshire and Shropshire, and at present only a few stations in oakwoods and beechwoods in Oxfordshire and Buckinghamshire are known. Normally only one or two plants appear at one site. The Ghost Orchid is a species from the British Red Data Book.

A rather more frequent saprophytic orchid of the European beech woods (also protected in a number of countries) is the smaller, pale yellow or faintly brownish 5—20 cm high **Coralroot Orchid** (*Corallorhiza trifida* Chatelain). The shape of the rhizome determined both its English and Latin name. The inconspicuous, tiny, yellowish green flowers bloom — according to the location and altitude of the habitat — from the end of spring to the beginning of summer. In Britain the Coralroot Orchid is rare and protected, confined to northern England and Scotland.

The Twayblades is the group of orchids whose distinguishing features are two big and broad, almost sessile, opposite leaves in the lower third of the stem. The **Lesser Twayblade** (*Listera cordata* (L.) R. Br.)

▽ The Wolfsbane (*Aconitum lycoctonum*) is a tall woodland perennial; the pale yellow flowers have a conspicuously high, cylindrical helmet which is usually narrow in the middle.

The Goatsbeard Spiraea (*Aruncus dioicus*) decorates ▷ mountain, foothill and sometimes also upland damp and shady gorges with its large, decorative leaves and rich inflorescence consisting of small pale yellow flowers.

The Austrian Leopard's Bane (*Doronicum austriacum*) ▷ ▷ is a tall perennial of mountain woodland, dwarf pine scrubs, spring areas and meadows. The golden yellow flower heads at the tops of branched stems are 5 to 6 cm in diameter.

has heart-shaped leaves which are only 1—3 cm long and broad. This perennial has only 5 to 15 cm high stems growing from slender roots without tubers. The short inflorescence is composed of very small, inconspicuous green or brownish red to violet flowers. They bloom through the summer — in June and July.

The Lesser Twayblade is basically a northern circumpolar plant growing in northern Eurasia and North America. In Europe it behaves like an Arctic-Alpine plant, which means that it is found in the far north where its range goes beyond the Arctic Circle; otherwise it occurs in the higher European mountains. In central Europe it can be found in the Alps, the Bavarian Forest, the Bohemian Forest, the Harz, the Thuringian Forest, the Ore Mountains, the Sudeten Mountains and in the higher Carpathian Mountain range. There are rare occurrences in the lower Czech-Moravian Highlands, in the relict spruce woods in Lusatia and on the Baltic Sea coast. On the Baltic it grows in peat-bog mossy pine woods, for example in the Slowinski National Park near Leba in Poland. Otherwise it is a characteristic species of spruce woods. In the Alps it is found up to 2,000 m above sea level. It also grows along the borders of raised peat-bogs. It is a shade-loving plant which grows in habitats with sufficient soil and air moisture. It roots in peaty soils and raw humus.

The Lesser Twayblade can be found throughout Britain, but it is declining and extinct in several counties due to the increase in public recreational activities on its habitats.

In the foothills and mountain forests several species of robust perennials can be found: the **Monkshoods** (*Aconitum*) of the Buttercup family (*Ranunculaceae*). Their erect stems with relatively dense alternate palmately divided leaves grow to a height of 50 cm — 1.5 m. They terminate in a rich leafy inflorescence of large 5-part flowers. The uppermost petal-like perianth segments form the prominent hood of a helmet.

The yellow-flowering **Wolfsbane** (*Aconitum lycoctonum* L. em. Koeller) has a long, cylindrical helmet which is narrow in the middle, and leaves with

broad leaflets whose edges overlap. It flowers from June to August. Like other species of the Monkshood, the Wolfsbane, because of a rich content of alkaloids, particularly in the rhizome, is highly poisonous. Its species name (Latin: *lycoctonus* = killing wolves) dates back to the Middle Ages when extracts from this herb were used to impregnate carcasses which were laid as traps for dangerous beasts of prey, particularly foxes and wolves. In ancient times in southern and central Europe, arrowheads were impregnated with the poisons of Wolfsbane.

Wolfsbane is a Eurasian species with a pre-Alpine range which means that the centre of its range is the Alps and the surrounding areas. The northern border of its range runs through central Europe from the central Rhineland to the Harz. It does not cross the Elbe in Germany; further eastward it roughly follows the northern border of the Czech Republic. It is a relatively rare plant of damp, mainly shaded habitats where it grows on fertile and humous soils. It is usually found in highlands, foothills and mountains. One comes across it in the undergrowth of riverine forests, in mixed woods in gorges, in beech woods and damp deciduous and mixed forests, as well as in meadows above the upper forest borders; in the Alps it climbs up to an altitude of over 2,000 m above sea level. In Britain the Wolfsbane is not native, it is only cultivated in gardens.

Monkshoods are remarkable plants for their contents and ornamental appearance. They were part of the arsenal used by medieval and possibly even earlier poisoners. The aconitine poison played a key role in the poisoning trial of Dr. George Henry Lamson in London in 1882, which became one of the milestones of the history of criminology and forensic medicine. However, Monkshoods are also important medicinal plants. The aconitine alkaloid, in appropriate doses, eases neuralgic pains, lowers fevers and eases phlegm. However, due to its lethal poison, Monkshood cannot be used in folk medicine. Any work with the plant (including cultivation) requires maximum caution; even the consumption of only a few grammes of the root will cause death in an adult by the paralysis of the central nervous system. In the wild the Monkshoods are a very precious genetic resource which is threatened by various effects of civilisation, above all the destruction of its habitats. In most European countries, all species of Monkshood are completely or at least partially protected by law. In country gardens the Monkshood has been grown since time immemorial and it has spread to become a naturalized species from these gardens.

In Britain only the **Monkshood** (*Aconitum anglicum* Stapf.) is native in woodland, meadows, scrub and stream margins. Also called 'Cat's tail' or 'Monk's coule' it is sometimes assigned to the species *Aconitum napellus* L. However, *Aconitum napellus* agg. is the collective name for about 10 species of mainly mountain Monkshoods. Monkshoods are variable plants. So far their taxonomic and nomenclature problems have not yet been resolved even in Europe. Of course, they deserve protection all the more.

The **Goatsbeard Spiraea** (*Aruncus dioicus* Kostel.) is a robust perennial which is 1−2 m tall. Its sparsely branched stems with 2-pinnate large leaves carry large top pannicled inflorescence composed of spiky racemes. The individual flowers are very small with yellowish white corollas only about 2 mm long. They flower at the beginning of the summer in June and July. At first sight hardly anyone would relate this plant to the Rose family (*Rosaceae*). The Goats-

beard Spiraea resembles cultivated Spiraeas and it was formerly classified under the *Spiraea* genus. It is often cultivated for decoration in gardens and parks. The fruits are small follicles and the seeds, weighing 0.00008 g, are among the lightest within European flora; air currents caused by sunrays suffice for transport of the seeds.

The range of this species, which is of a somewhat pre-Alpine character, extends from the Pyrenees to the Caucasus. Its north-western border runs through central Europe. The Goatsbeard Spiraea requires fertile, humous soil (perhaps even in scree) on damp and shady sites. It is not greatly abundant in the hills and highlands on central Europe, but mainly grows in mixed gorge maple woods and foothill beech woods up to about 1,500 m above sea level. In Britain it is only naturalized.

In Europe the Goatsbeard Spiraea appears on red lists only locally and in lower threat categories. It is protected by law — fully or partially — in Switzerland, Austria and Germany. It deserves protection as a genetic resource with use in ornamental gardening. In the open countryside, the decorative plant attracts visitors to its sites. Formerly it was also used as a medicinal plant.

Not many gardens exist where in the spring you cannot find the Leopard's Banes — perennials of the Daisy family (*Compositae*) which look like yellow ox-eye daisies. Even in this ornamental plant the basic genetic resource originates from the wild. The European Leopard's Banes are high mountain plants. One comes across them mostly above the upper tree limit.

A species of mountain forests in the **Austrian Leopard's Bane** (*Doronicum austriacum* Jacq.). It is a tall perennial, up to 1.5 m high, with erect, angular, sparsely branched stems. The flower heads on long,

thin stalks with golden yellow ray florets measure about 5 cm in diameter. They flower in the summer months — July and August.

The Austrian Leopard's Bane is a southern European plant widespread mainly in the Alps. Through their foothills it penetrates to Austria and Hungary. It is quite common in the Carpathians and is also found in the Bavarian Forest and on the opposite side of the border in the Bohemian Forest. The northern range border reaches the Orlické Mountains and the highland of Králický Sněžník in the Czech Republic. It grows on fertile, sufficiently damp, loamy and clay humous soils, usually in shady foothill and mountain beech woods and fir beech woods, most often around springs and streams. It also climbs to the dwarf mountain pine belt and mountain meadows up to an altitude of 1,500 m above sea level. This conspicuous decorative plant is often damaged in the wild by being picked for bouquets. It is protected by law in the Czech Republic and in Hungary.

The Leopard's Banes are not native in British flora. However in the countryside, especially in eastern Scotland, one sees in woods, scrub and at the roadsides the Leopard's Bane (*Doronicum pardalianches* L.). The medium to tall, hairy perennial with heart-shaped leaves is naturalized in Britain and quite abundant in localised areas.

Basically a woodland species climbing to the mountain fir-beech woods is the delicate '**Alpine Violet**' or **Sowbread** (*Cyclamen purpurascens* Mill.), the Primrose family (*Primulaceae*). This perennial has an orbicular tuber under the ground from which a rosette grows of hibernating leaves with long stalks and fleshy, heart-shaped round blades. The blades are purplish on the under-side, dark green and whitish marbled on top. Charming carmine-pink flowers of 1.5 to 2 cm in length on thin stalks (5—15 cm) grow directly from the rosette. They bloom at the end of the summer, particularly in August and September. When they ripen into fruit capsules, the flower buries the fruit in coiling movements into dry, fallen leaves, where the capsule hibernates. Its seeds do not ripen until the following year.

Sowbreads are important garden ornamentals and thus the sowbread represents a valuable genetic natural resource. The genetic base for houseplants is the Mediterranean Persian Sowbread (*Cyclamen persicum* Mill.). The (European) Sowbread contains interesting substances, particularly the poisonous glycoside cyclamin. It was used as a medicinal plant to cure stomach and intestinal problems, externally to reduce swelling, against gout and the treatment of wounds. Because the drug encourages digestion, ancient nations used the tubers for pig fodder, from which the English plant name derives.

The name 'Alpine Violet' indicates the geographical distribution of the species whose centre of range is in the Alps, particularly in the eastern Alps. In Germany the Sowbread is only found in Bavaria in the Berchtesgaden Alps, from where it was washed down alongside the rivers as far as the Danube. The other occurrences are secondary and not original. It is widespread in Austria from where it penetrates western Hungary, north into southern Bohemia and southern Moravia. Its most northern stations are in the Moravian karst north of Brno. It is more rare than abundant in Switzerland — in the Alps and the Jura, from where it spreads into eastern France. In Britain the Sowbread is cultivated only in gardens.

The Sowbread grows particularly in calciphilous beech woods, but can also be found in pre-Alpine pine woods on limestone ground, and descends into

Distribution of the Common Yew in Europe.

thermophilous hornbeam-oak woods (southern Moravia). In northern Switzerland it is a local characteristic species of deciduous woods with a predominance of lime, but it can also be found in Alpine spruce woods. It grows in semi-shade on fertile humous, mainly calcareous and stony soils. It ascends to about 1,000 m above sea level. It is protected by law in Switzerland, Germany, Austria, the Czech Republic and Hungary.

In the Slovak Republic's Carpathian mountains a Slovak endemic can be found growing in similar conditions which is called the **Fatra Sowbread** (*Cyclamen fatrense* Halda et Soják), and this is a strictly protected species. It differs in its leaves from the Sowbread as they are a shiny deep green on top, without marbling, and are also smaller.

A similar, also strictly protected species is the **Ivy-leaved Sowbread** (*Cyclamen hederifolium* Aiton) a southern and western European species, in central Europe occurring in southern Switzerland, in the Rhône valley in Valais. It differs from other European species mainly in the shape of its leaves, which are similar to those of the ivy with their lobed, pointed, green and grey blades. Pale pink flowers appear before or with the young leaves. They bloom from August to November. This is the most commonly cultivated Cyclamen in open gardens in Britain, sometimes becoming naturalized. Two or three stations in woodland, however, are known in Kent considered by botanists to be most probably native. Two are protected by Sites of Special Scientific Interest. The Ivy-leaved Sowbread is included in the British Red Data Book.

The coniferous **Common Yew** (*Taxus baccata* L.) of the ancient Yew family (*Taxaceae*) often grows alongside the wild cyclamens in the under-

141

growth, for example in the Protected Landscape Area of the Moravian karst in the Czech Republic in the lower tree canopy of beech woods. It is a relatively short tree (sometimes just a bush when growing on rocks) of up to 20 m in height with a dense, elongated pyramidal to irregular crown. The trunk is covered by brownish red bark, later flaking with greyish brown scales, and is often complemented with subsidiary trunks. The needles are shiny dark green on top and lighter in colour on the underside. The yew is a dioecious plant so male and female flowers do not grow together on one tree. The male specimens are coloured in early spring (March – April) by stamens of yellowish green male flowers. The inconspicuous, bud-like female flowers develop at the end of the summer and in the autumn into fruit of blood red pulpy cups which are open on top and contain blackish brown seeds.

Since ancient times the Common Yew has been enveloped in legend and superstition. This arises from its somewhat bleak appearance (the ancient tree of sadness, still planted in cemeteries) and above all its poison. It contains a mixture of several substances mainly the poisonous alkaloid, taxine. This is found in all its parts except the pulpy cup, its deceptive red berry. The yew played an important role in folk magic and in primitive folk medicine. For example, in Slovakia yew-tree broth was used to clean out wounds from rabid animal bites or they were sprinkled with minced yew timber. It was also used as an abortive lotion and therefore was – as records from Slovakia show – intentionally and sometimes even ritually destroyed with the participation of a priest. The yew has good-quality, highly durable, hard timber which was used in the building industry especially for water constructions. In the Middle Ages bows were made from yew wood and this is the reason why yew trees were often planted around castles. It is said that, during the Danish occupation of the Darss Peninsula in Germany, all the local yews were felled to prevent the Slavs to have bows.

The European Yew's geographic distribution extends into southern Scandinavia and covers the British Isles. This indicates a clear oceanic tendency in its occurrence (although the yew does not grow in the wild in most of France). The eastern border of its range runs through central Poland. Naturally the yew tree still occurs in central Europe mostly among scree and on rocky, mainly valley hillsides, in habitats with sufficient humidity, i.e. in beech woods and fir-beech woods or in other types of deciduous and mixed woodland. For example in the Swiss Jura and the Alpine foothills there is the plant forest association *Taxo-Fagetum* of yew-beech woods growing on steep hillsides. In the mountains this rare conifer grows to an altitude of about 1,500 m above sea level.

Islets of natural or semi-natural woods in many

places in central Europe became the reason for declaring nature reserves such as in the deep rocky valleys of the central Bohemian Vltava and Berounka rivers. There is a remarkable natural habitat of the yew on the chalk cliffs of the Jasmund National Park on the island of Rügen in northern Germany. Yews belong to the botanical treasures in the Weltenburger Enge Reserve in the gorge of the Danube river in the Franconian Jura in western Germany. The biggest central European site of yews is the Harmanecká Valley (nature reserve) in the Protected Landscape Area of the Veľká Fatra in Slovakia. Some 160,000 trees have been counted there.

The yew is protected by law in the Czech and the Slovak Republics, Germany, Austria and Poland. However, in nature reserves it is being extensively damaged by game grazing. Deer are especially keen on it as the yew's poison has no effect on them. There is also an unfortunate tendency, especially in the Czech Republic, of carving various decorative articles (so-called objets trouvés) from contorted yew trunks and branches. The yew tree lives for a long time, although it has been proved that some records of thousand-year-old trees are exaggerated because they were attained by counting the annual growth rings on the stumps of trees which have grown together with side trunks. Nevertheless scattered old and large yews survive as remains of native woods or of those planted by people. They are particularly frequent in Britain, where the Common Yew is widespread throughout, both native and cultivated.

The yew is often cultivated in gardens and parks, church yards, amenity woods and hedges as an ornamental conifer. Up to a certain extent it is resistant to smoke gases and therefore it is recommended for planting in an urban environment. (However, in some countries, e.g. Germany, due to the strong poi-

son of the tree, it is prohibited to plant it near schools and children's playgrounds.)

Many cultivars have been bred and yews are popular trees for cutting into various shapes, whether in hedgerows or as solitary bushes and trees. Moreover these conifers, contrasting with their dark green colour against the lighter green vegetation, contribute towards the aesthetic effect of the landscape.

The attentive reader will probably have noticed that among the abbreviations of authorities who were the first to describe certain plant species, following the scientific (Latin) names of the given species, the abbreviation authority 'L.' predominates. This abbreviation is none other than that of the father of systematic botany, the Swede Carolus Linnaeus. However, not many people know the plant which bears the name of this great botanist in its generic name. In his native Sweden and in other countries in the far European north we come across this plant almost all the time, not only in woods, but also on porcelain, glasses and other articles of everyday use or souvenirs. This plant belongs to the Honeysuckle family (*Caprifoliaceae*) and is called the **Twin Flower** (*Linnaea borealis* L.).

The Twin Flower is a slender, short perennial herb or sub-shrub, with creeping thin woody stems with evergreen opposite (5—15 cm) ascendant to erect oval leaves. From them short branches grow carrying 1 to 3 campanulate, nodding, pleasantly scented white or pinkish flowers. Most frequently the flowers are borne in pairs which is reflected by the English name of the plant. It blooms from June to August.

This delicate living monument to Carolus Linnaeus is quite commonly widespread in the coniferous woods of northern Eurasia and North America. It can be found in pine woods on the Arctic Circle in Finland and Sweden just as in the Arolla Pine taiga of northern Mongolia or in the zone of northern coniferous woods in the USA and Canada. In central Europe it is found on various sites in the Alpine spruce woods and rarely in the highest Carpathian mountains ranges. The Twin Flower is almost extinct in the lower European highlands. Plants from the Iser Mountains in the Czech Republic today exist only as yellowing herbarial specimens, and in the Giant Mountains the species probably survives only on the Polish side of the range. In Poland the Twin Flower is found particularly in the eastern part of the country, e.g. as a relict in the Roztoczanski National Park where our photo was taken. Occurrences in pine woods, even natural ones in northern Germany and the adjacent part of Poland, are sometimes considered as secondary: the species was probably brought over by migratory birds from Scandinavia. The Twin Flower is protected by law in Germany and Poland. It is a popular rock garden plant. In Britain, the Twin Flower is very rare (although not included in the British Red Data Book), found only in eastern Scotland, where it is a distinct floral feature of the Caledonian pine woods.

Of the whole series of Gentians native in Europe, the **Willow Gentian** (*Gentiana asclepiadea* L.) appears at the herb canopy of mountain woodland. This species has become the symbol of the Czech Giant Mountains (Krkonoše) National Park. This 50 cm — 1 m high perennial gained its Latin species name from its similarity (in the non-flowering state, the leafy stems) to the species of the genus *Asclepias* of the Swallow-wort family (*Asclepidaceae*). The flowers, which bloom from August to September, sit in numbers of 1 to 3, usually in pairs, in the axil of the upper leaves. Its trumpet-shaped campanulate corollas are about 5 cm long, of a wonderful dark azure blue colour with mauve dots inside or, more rarely, white.

The centre of the range of the Willow Gentian are

the Alps from where it extends as a great rarity into the far western part of Hungary. It grows in the highest Carpathian mountains, in northern Italy, Corsica, the Balkan mountains, locally in Asia Minor and the Caucasus. On the northern border of its range it is found in the Iser mountains and the Giant Mountains in the Czech Republic and Poland. In central Europe it grows up to an altitude from about 400 to almost 2,000 m above sea level, in beech woods, fir-beech woods and spruce woods as well as in boggy meadows with the Purple Moor-grass (in the foothills of the Alps — the Alpenvorland) above the upper forest limit in the mountain pine belt, in mountain meadows and pastures. In Britain, the Willow Gentian is not native, but is widely cultivated in gardens in a choice of different forms.

In all central European countries the Willow Gentian is protected by law. The stem and underground parts contain bitter substances and therefore it used to be gathered — although to a lesser extent than other species — as a medicinal, and above all as an aromatic plant for use in the production of Gentian liqueurs and brandies. The picking and uprooting of the conspicuous flowers for bouquets was formerly considered the greatest threat to this species in the wild. Today, however, it is threatened much more by the recreational and sports activities in the European mountains. The legal species protection is usually a very weak tool against damage and destruction. Territorial protection and strict implementation of the conservation rules in national and nature mountain parks and protected areas must be reinforced. In the northern islet of range — in the Iser and Giant Mountains — there are still numerous populations of the Willow Gentian, but these are threatened by acid rain causing the collapse of the existing ecosystems.

The symbol of the National Park (and also the UNESCO Biosphere Reserve) Bavarian Forest in Germany is another decorative plant of mountain woods, the **Mountain Snowbell** (*Soldanella montana* Willd.) of the Primrose family (*Primulaceae*). It is a low perennial (10—25 cm high when in flower) with a ground rosette of leathery, stalked, orbicular, kidney-shaped leaves. From May to June the leafless stems bear an umbel of 3 to 6 — about 1.5 cm long flowers — bluish violet fringed bells.

The centre of the range of the Mountain Snowbell is in the spruce woods of the Bohemian Forest and its Bavarian and Austrian counterparts. A special association of Snowbell spruce woods — the *Soldanello-Piceetum* was even described here. Here the Mountain Snowbell ascends to an altitude of about 1,500 m above sea level and is often found in colonies in damp humous soils, in shady habitats. South of the Bohemian Forest in appears in the Alpine foothills, in the north it penetrates sporadically into Bohemia where it grows in lower highlands (500—600 m above sea level) alongside forest brooks and around springs.

It is a protected species in the Czech Republic and has become a symbol of the State Nature Conservancy of the district of Prachatice in the Bohemian Forest. The plant is a popular rockery plant, so it is often collected by gardeners in the wild. If growing outside protected territories, it is also damaged by the destruction of its habitats due to intensive forestry and sometimes even farming.

A species similar to the Mountain Snowbell is the **Hungarian Snowbell** (*Soldanella hungarica* Simonka) which grows in woodland in the higher Carpathian mountain range and can sometimes be found in eastern Austria. Above the upper mountain tree limit in the Alps grow the delicate Alpine rock species the **Alpine Snowbell** (*Soldanella alpina* L.), the **Smallest Snowbell** (*Soldanella minima* Hoppe) and the **Small Snowbell** (*Soldanella pusilla* Baumg. The **Carpathian Snowbell** (*Soldanella carpatica* Vierh.) is found in the highest Carpathians.

An ornamental which can be found in the highest belt of coniferous woodland, already open with a well developed shrub canopy, is the **Alpine Clematis** (*Clematis alpina* (L.) Mill.) of the Buttercup family (*Ranunculaceae*). This 1—3 cm long, deciduous woody climber, is one of a few actual central European liana plants. The long-stalked leaves are once or twice ternate. In their axils on long thin stalks grow solitary flowers with 4 violet to light blue, petal-like sepals of 3—4 cm in length which have fine hairs on the exterior. The attractiveness of the flowers, which bloom from May to July, is increased by the large number of stamens with distinct yellow anthers. The fruit — achenes with long curved silky styles — are also decorative.

The Alpine Clematis, according to its general geographic distribution, is an Arctic-Alpine species. In central Europe it is found in both main mountain ranges, in the Alps and the Carpathians. It grows in coniferous woods, scrub and in the mountain pine belt up to an altitude of 2,000 m above sea level. However, in the Carpathians we know of sites located only several hundred metres above sea level, in deep rock gorges such as in the Protected Landscape Area and Biosphere Reserve in Slovakian karst in Slovakia. The Alpine Clematis requires fertile, humous, especially calcareous soils. It is protected by law in Switzerland, Austria, the Czech and Slovak Republics, in Poland and in Hungary where it grows peripherally.

The Alpine Clematis often scrambles round the 'Alpine roses' — Rhododendrons. Rhododendrons are shrubs of the Heath family (*Ericaceae*). The genus has about 1,200 species, of which about 700 are cultivated in parks, gardens, greenhouses and pots and hundreds of cultivars have originated from them. The genetic natural resource of Rhododendrons is, therefore, of considerable importance in gardening apart from its important contribution to the beauty of the landscape, especially when the bushes grow in entire extensive growths.

The **Alpenrose** (*Rhododendron ferrugineum* L.) often creates large groves. It is a low evergreen shrub (up to 1 m) with elongated, 2—4 cm long leaves, shiny deep green on top and with dense rust coloured scales on the underside (hence the species name), with revolute leaf margins. The numerous top umbels are composed of 6 to 12, sometimes up to 30 trumpet-shaped campanulate flowers with purplish red, 2 cm long corollas. The flowers bloom through the summer — from June to August.

The Alpenrose is an Alpine species also found in the Pyrenees and the Balkans. It grows on non-calcareous, humous, stony and sufficiently damp soil in the undergrowth of open spruce woods, pine woods and open Arolla Pine woodland in the mountain pine belt and in scrub above the upper tree limit. The upper limit of its occurrence in the Alps lies more than 2,000 m above sea level, but the plant often descends through spruce woodland and boggy pine woodland to the Alpine foothills. In most European countries where it grows — in Switzerland, Germany and Austria — it is protected by law.

In those countries another Alpine species is also strictly protected: the **Hairy Alpenrose** (*Rhododendron hirsutum* L.). Unlike the Alpenrose, its leaves do not have reddish scales on the underside and they are hairy on the margins. This species is calciphilous. Both Alpenroses were once used in folk medicine. The yellow *Rhododendron luteum* Sweet is strictly protected in Poland. It is a more robust bush, 1.2 to 2 m high, yellow flowering with deciduous leaves. It can be found in much of eastern and south-eastern Europe, on the Black Sea coast and in the Caucasus.

It grows in undergrowth and on the margins of deciduous forests. It has an overpowering scent. It is widely cultivated in gardens and has been used as a primary genetic base for the selection of Rhododendron cultivars.

There is no native Rhododendron in the British flora. But the *Rhododendron ponticum* L., an evergreen shrub of 5 m, forming large patches, is very common. Its natural range lies in western Asia and south-eastern Europe, but it is widely naturalized in Britain (as well as in Belgium and France). The shrub with large deep shiny green leaves and 4—6 cm long pinkish flowers, was once commonly planted in amenity woodland and game coverts. Now firmly established, it spreads forming dense thickets in which little else can live. The case of the Rhododendron is not one of the threatened native species: on the contrary, it is a naturalized stranger which is often becoming a menace and is difficult to control.

Many ornamental ferns which are in need of protection can be found in beech woods, and in foothill and mountain mixed woodland. Among them is the conspicuous **Hart's-tongue** (*Phyllitis scolopendrium* (L.) Newm.) of the Spleenwort family (*Aspleniaceae*). It is an evergreen fern with undivided, entire shiny, green, tongue-shaped leaves of 15 to 50 cm in length. The brown sori on the underside are linear, transverse and parallel in two rows, one on each side of the distinctive midrib.

This species, which has sub-Mediterranean and sub-Atlantic tendencies, is distributed across Eu-

◁ The Hart's Tongue (*Phyllitis scolopendrium*) is a decorative rock, calcicole fern with short stalked leaves over 0.5 m in length; its shiny green, undivided, broadly linear lanceolate blades resemble a tongue.

▽ The Mountain Shield-fern (*Polystichum lonchitis*), with leathery, simply pinnate leaves, grows on rocks and scree in the undergrowth of foothill and mountain forests; it also grows above the upper tree line.

The Flat Clubmoss (*Diphasium complanatum*) has ▷ spore cases bearing spikes on 2—10 cm long thin stems from furcate branches, which are covered with narrow, greyish green unequal leaves like roof slates.

rope from the British Isles and south-western Norway to the Iberian Peninsula and through the Balkans and the Black Sea to Asia. It also grows in the Far East and in North America. The north-eastern border of its range runs through central Europe from the lower Rhineland to the Harz and Thuringia to the Elbe Sandstone Highland. It descends to the Danube (today in Bohemia the species is missing), it runs through central Moravia and further on eastward along the edge of the Carpathians at the Polish-Slovak state border. The Hart's-tongue is a calciphilous species and requires considerable humidity and shade in its habitat. It grows on rocks and scree in the undergrowth of gorge ash maple woods and calciphilous beech woods from lowlands to mountains. Within reach of a coastal climate in western Europe it sometimes also grows on walls, stone bridges and particularly on the internal edges of walled wells. It is a highly ornamental fern often cultivated for its beauty. Formerly it was also used as a medicinal

plant. It is protected by law in all central European countries with the exception of Hungary.

In contrasty to most central European countries, in Britain the Hart's-tongue is a widespread and common species, mainly abundant in uplands, rather sparse in lowlands.

The **Mountain Shield-fern** (*Polystichum lonchitis* (L.) Roth.) of the Male-fern family (*Aspidiaceae*) represents the ideal image of a beautiful fern. Its green, leathery, hibernating leaves, which are about half a metre long, with narrow (5 cm at most) blades, simply pinnate from 20 to 50 pairs of leaflets, look as if they have been imprinted on stiff paper. The circular, large sori are scattered in the upper part of the leaves.

It is an Arctic-Alpine circumpolar species. In Europe it is found in highlands and mountains (it does not grow in lowlands) where it grows on rocks and scree mainly on limestone, in the undergrowth of gorge maple woods and fir beech woods. In high mountains it is found above the upper tree limit at an altitude of almost 2,500 m above sea level. In Germany and the Czech Republic it is a very rare species registered on the red lists in the highest threat category. It is protected by law in Hungary. In Britain the Mountain Shield-fern is rather rare, occurring only in the mountains of Scotland, northern England, north Wales and Ireland.

In the mountain forests of Europe several other species can also be found of the same genus, which do not, however, much resemble the Mountain Shield-fern. Some appear on central European red lists or on the list of species protected by law or decrees on nature conservation. These are the **Hard Shield-fern** (*Polystichum aculeatum* (L.) Roth.), the **Soft Shield-fern** (*Polystichum setiferum* (Forskal) T. Moore ex Woynar) and the **Braun's Shield-fern** (*Polystichum braunii* (Spenn.) Fee).

At first sight one could confuse the Mountain Shield-fern with an equally decorative species of coniferous and mixed woodland, the **Hard Fern** (*Blechum spicant* (L.) Roth.). However, apart from having similar hibernating ground leaves it also has in summer different erect fruiting fronds with narrow linear segments vertically erect in the centre of the tuft. Growing in shady woods and sheltered areas on moorland or heathland, the Hard Fern is still quite common in Britain.

Some **Clubmoss** (*Lycopodiaceae*) plants in European flora are also rare and deserve protection. In the Czech and the Slovak Republics and in Austria all the species are protected by law.

The **Flat Clubmoss** (*Diphasium complanatum* (L.) Rothm.) is a perennial, greyish green plant forming rounded colonies spreading at their margins. The furcately branched, flat, overground branches are densely covered with tiny, scaly, compressed leaves of equal size. At the end of summer, from August to September, 2—6 spore-cases bearing spikes of 2—3 cm in length grow on 2—10 cm long ends of branches — 'thin stalks'. Of all the representatives of this genus, this is the most common species, but it cannot be said that it grows in great abundance. It is a typical species of damp, mossy pine woods and spruce woods growing on humous, often peaty but often also sandy or stony acid soils which are low in nutrients from lowlands right up to medium mountain levels. It was once recorded in Britain in Gloucestershire and Worcestershire; otherwise the western border of this northern circumpolar species run west of the Rhine river.

A number of other species of the relatively variable genus *Diphasium* are found in Europe and these appear on red lists and lists of protected species. The **Issler's Clubmoss** (*Diphasium issleri* (Rouy) Holub) has also been included on the European red list. At the end of its branches this species always has one spike.

In Britain's highlands and mountains the **Alpine Clubmoss** (*Diphasiastrum alpinum* (L.) Holub) with solitary sessile spikes grows in open moss- and lichen-dominated communities. This tuft- and cluster-forming Clubmoss is very rare in some British regions.

MOUNTAIN MEADOWS, PASTURES, ROCKS AND SCREES

The Alps are the largest mountain system in Europe. The photograph shows the Triglav National Park in Slovenia.

The dizzy heights and stunning views of the mountains have always held a special attraction for man. In the steep, rocky mountain walls man would seek and find crystals as clear as the water of mountain torrents and other precious stones. However, in mountain shingles, grasslands, rocks and screes man was and still is drawn to the living jewels in the form of mountain flowers. The high mountains hold the greatest gems of European flora.

This last chapter provides an overview of a selection of central and west European mountain flora which is in need of protection, i.e. Alpine plants which occur mainly above the upper treeline. However, in comparison with the wealth of species growing there, this is just a small selection.

At altitudes where climatic conditions — cold and wind — do not allow the existence of trees or woods, the sole extensive European areas of herb vegetation which have developed are treeless salt marshes, peatbogs, swamps and steppes in the lowlands and uplands. The core of this vegetation is in the Alpine belt. Above it, where the average annual snowfall exceeds rainfall, nival vegetation appears. Closed plant communities give way to individual plants in rocky crevices or in protected scree, sometimes even on rocky islets protruding from the glaciers or granular snow fields. These plants grow as high as the eternal snow-line.

High mountain plants are adapted to their harsh environment. They are exposed to low temperatures, winds, thick snow cover and strong sunlight. They must be able to live, flower and bear fruit within a short period of time, usually during the few months between the thaw of the last snows and the arrival of the new. Their characteristic features are low, creeping, often densely tufted to cushion-forming growth and large, richly and conspicuously coloured flowers. Due to the fact that the climatic conditions in the mountains are similar to the climate of the far north, many of the same plant species found in European mountains at an altitude of about 2,000 m above sea level also grow in northern Scandinavia on rocks at maybe 2 m above sea level. So phytogeographers call these plants Arctic-Alpine or (if the centre of their range lies in more southern areas) Alpine-Arctic.

There are three high mountain systems in central and western Europe. These are the Alps, the Carpathians and the Pyrenees. Today there are no longer any glaciers in the Carpathians or in the Pyrenees and their highest peaks do not reach the eternal snow-line, but nival vegetation can be found there. One sometimes comes across high-mountain flowers at lower altitudes. These are plants which have been washed down from the mountains along valley rivers, as in the foothills of the Alps, where they grow on moving gravel banks at sections not yet secured by dams and river canalizations. Some species have survived as relicts in lower, so-called inversive areas, in deep rock gorges, for example in the Slovak Carpathians. In the Austrian and Bavarian Alpine foothills one comes across such species in relict habitats in raised peat-bogs and in grassland. High mountain plants are also found in the Swiss Jura.

However, there are also medium mountain ranges in central and western Europe with altitudes from 1,000 to 1,500 m above sea level, which therefore do not reach the sub-Alpine, let alone the Alpine belts as indicated by the vegetation levels of the Alps, Pyrenees and Carpathians. These regions are the Massif Central, the Vosges, the Black Forest, the Harz, the Bavarian and Bohemian Forests, the Ore Mountains and particularly the Sudeten mountains — the Giant Mountains, Králický Sněžník and

149

Jeseníky Mountains. Nevertheless, even here one can find, more rarely of course, occurrence of high mountain flora. The local climatic conditions cause the decrease in altitude of the tree-line, so the mountain ridges and peaks of about 1,200 metres above sea level are treeless. An altogether special phenomenon in central European (and perhaps other) highlands are the so-called anemo-orographic systems, i.e. the complex influenced by mountain relief (particularly in the chequered valleys which remained after the glaciation) and air currents. In areas where these systems exist one can find vegetation of the Alpine belt at lower altitudes (about 1,000 m above sea level).

In Britain there are mountains with the flora and vegetation of Arctic-Alpine character in northern Wales and in Scotland. They do not reach the altitudes of the Alps, but because of the climate, this vegetation occurs at lower altitudes, such as in the Welsh Snowdonia. An exclusively British incidence is the occurrence of small refuge areas, where alpine and arctic plant communities, persisting from the end of the Ice Age, are now isolated by large distances. The Burren in western Ireland and Upper Teesdale in northern England are the most famous examples of such relict vegetation.

The mountains are sometimes described as the last large remnants of 'original' areas untouched by human activities. However even here, over the course of many centuries, man has made an impact on the mountain countryside, sometimes with rather far-reaching consequences. Although the mining of minerals which has taken place in the mountains for centuries did not have a terribly destructive effect on the vegetation, man then tried to utilize economically the extensive high mountain grasslands. So hay was mowed and dried on mountain meadows and there was also sheep and cattle grazing. This activity did have a significant impact on the vegetation. Today there are many disputes among botanists and ecologists with regard to the former natural tree-line, because this has been artificially decreased in altitude mostly by grazing or by the extension of the mountain meadows and pastures. In the Alps and Carpathians in extensive areas of woodland, often of Arolla and Dwarf Mountain Pines, on mountain slopes and lower mountain ridges trees were felled and these woodlands were converted into pastures. However, with much too intensive grazing, the cattle trample the slopes, disturb the vegetation and pull up the turf, so that deep cuts appear in the soil, leading to erosion. Also the composition of plant communities is changing. Many species, sensitive to trampling, grazing or even to the effect of animal excrement are disappearing and giving way to plants which domestic livestock avoids because they are poisonous, tough or prickly. Round about the mountain huts nitrophilous (dependent on rich nitrogen) growths of mountain ruderal plants are spreading: Docks and often also Nettles.

The modern age also brought, after the miner and farmer, the hiker, tourist and later the sportsman. These people picked the mountain flowers for bouquets, transferred plants to the foothills and lowlands and made miniature imitations of the mountain landscape with its flora in their own gardens — the rock-garden. The first efforts of nature conservation in the high mountain regions were aimed at protecting the prettiest and most attractive mountain plants from being picked and uprooted. The first ordinances on plant species protection began to be issued for the Austrian Alps in 1880, for some mountain species in the Giant Mountains in 1890, Gentians in the Bavarian Alps, Alpenrose in some Swiss cantons, etc. However, the wealth of high mountain flora began to be literally pillaged by herbalists who believed in the miraculous curative power of these attractive herbs or used their aromatic substances to add to the taste of liqueurs produced at home, in private factories or even in Alpine monasteries. It seems likely that the behaviour of herbalists really did result in the extinction of some of the most persecuted species, at least locally. For example in the Giant Mountains in the 18th century, the Silesian 'Guild of Laboratory Technicians' systematically exploited medicinal plants.

The development of nature conservation has brought with it the establishment in European mountains of important protected areas, usually large-scale ones (over 1,000 hectares). In 1914 the Swiss National Park was established in Engadin as a new type of national park in the form of a strict nature reserve. Today the area of this protected Alpine territory measures 16,887 hectares and in 1979 it was declared a Biosphere Reserve within the international UNESCO Programme 'Man and the Biosphere'. The Austrian Alpine protected areas Gurgler Kamm and Gossenkollensee near Innsbruck are also Biosphere Reserves. The great Austrian National Park in the Hohe Tauern has been completed only recently. The 'foundation stone' (the declaration of the first 2,500 hectares) was laid in 1983. In many cases European mountain national parks and reserves are protected bilaterally on either side of the frontier between two countries which is often formed by mountain ridge or valley. For example the Slovak-Polish High Tatra National

Park in the Carpathians and the Czech-Polish Giant Mountains, are both unsurpassed in their botanic values. The recent political changes in Europe have brought new challenges and opportunities, in particular behind the former 'iron curtain'. One of the largest reserves in eastern Germany — the region of the Harz mountains with the highest mountain of Brocken (1,980 hectares) — has recently become a national park. The Bavarian Forest National Park has now been joined by its younger transboundary counterpart in the Czech Šumava (Bohemian Forest) National Park established in 1991, and both parks are now cooperating closely. In western Germany the Alpine Berchtesgaden National Park was not declared until 1978. It has an area of 20,000 hectares and its core is the former Königsee Reserve at one of the largest and most beautiful Alpine lakes. This region is also famous for its botanic rarities.

Hence protection of areas is the right solution and must therefore be reinforced. So far central and west European mountain flora has put up a successful resistance against the direct persecution by people thanks to strict territorial protection as in the High Tatras in Slovakia and Poland. However, the growth of tourism could prove fatal to many species and communities. This particularly applies to winter recreation and sports. Mountain hotels, ski lifts, pistes and other facilities are destroying vegetation on a large scale. There is also another danger. Grass

151

must be sown artificially on mountain ski pistes due to erosion. This involves the use of mixtures of exotic plant species and cultivars which threaten to disturb the local vegetation, i.e. cause the corrosion of the local genetic biodiversity. Comprehensive measures must be undertaken to enable people to enjoy the mountains at the same time as supporting the mountain plants and their communities: for they too contribute to the enjoyment of people.

The plant symbol of the mountains has always been the **Edelweiss** (*Leontopodium alpinum* Cass.). This perennial of the Daisy family (*Compositae*) would appear to defy all the norms and rules of botanical families. The 5 to 25 cm hight plant with simple, erect, sparsely leaved stems which are solitary or in tufts, is covered with a white down and has small, yellowish flowers of 3 to 6 cm in diameter in dense clusters. The Edelweiss flowers in July and August.

It is a distinctive Alpine species of the European high mountains. Other similar small species are found further east in Siberia, the Altai mountains and in the Far East. In Europe the Edelweiss is widespread in the Alps, the Carpathians, the Jura and southwards from them. It usually grows at a height of 1,700 to 2,500 m above sea level. In the Swiss Valais canton it occurs as high as 3,400 m above sea level. By contrast, in the rock gorges of the Slovak Carpathians it also grows at lower altitudes of about 1,000 m above sea level, e.g. in the Slovenský Raj (Slovak Paradise) National Park and Muráňská Planina (Plain) Protected Landscape Area. It also sometimes grows as 'a washed-down plant' in Alpine river valleys. The Edelweiss is a distinctive, calciphilous plant.

It grows almost exclusively on limestone and dolomitic grounds as a characteristic species of the union of high mountain communities of the Varied Sesleria (*Sesleria varia*) — *Seslerion variae* or other related species of Sesleria.

The common name of this decorative herb, adopted from German by other languages including English ('refined white' — Edelweiss), came about only at the end of the 18th century with the start of mountain tourism. The Edelweiss looks best in rock crevices, and often exists on steep rocky cliffs which are only accessible to mountaineers. There are various legends and stories which relate how people paid with their life after picking the Edelweiss by falling down a sheer cliff wall. Mountain people used to pick the Edelweiss for decoration and sale, so that the plant in many mountain regions either became extinct or was forced out to the most inaccessible rocky habitats. In those places where strict conservation measures were enforced, such as the prohibition of grazing or even the closing of tourist paths in the limestone Belianské Tatras in the Slovak Tatra National Park the Alpine Edelweiss did relocate from the rocks sometimes even to the floristically rich grasslands on shallow soils covering rock and scree. Another measure carried out in the Tatra National Park is the cultivation of the Edelweiss in special gardens. All live or pressed edelweiss souvenirs come from here.

The deceptive stellate 'flower' of the Edelweiss decorates the packing of various products. Mountaineering associations bear the sign of the Edelweiss in their logos. Mountain hotels and restaurants are named after it. In short the popularity of this 'mountain queen' is immense. The Edelweiss was once also used in folk medicine or rather in magic (the exorcism of evil spirits from cow-sheds in the Swiss Alps with edelweiss smoke). The plant can normally be obtained from gardening firms specializing in rock plants, although they do sometimes sell the similar, less tomentose Siberian Edelweiss (*Leontopodium sibiricum* Dc.). The popularity of the Edelweiss as a symbol of the mountains led to the planting of this species in lower central European highlands and uplands (e.g. in Czech border mountains). The Edelweiss can remain in such a secondary location only

for a limited period of time, not permanently. When being cultivated on rockeries, it must have calcareous, finely humous, but strong stony soil and a dry, sunny position without any competition from other plants otherwise it would lose its most characteristic and most decorative white tomentose look. The Edelweiss is protected by law in all European countries in which it is native.

Gentians of the Gentian family (*Gentianaceae*) are also often used as high mountain symbols, particularly the very decorative (and equally popular as rock plants) low gentians with short stems and large bells of blue. One such species is the **Trumpet Gentian** (*Gentiana clusii* Pers. et Song.). It has a similar area of distribution to the Edelweiss, growing on the same habitats, on calcareous ground and often together with it. One exception for the Alpine foothills is the quite typical occurrence of the Trumpet Gentian on wet meadows with the Davall Sedge and in lower altitudes in dry grassland together with the Upright Brome.

The Trumpet Gentian is a hairless perennial, only 2—10 cm high with a ground leaf rosette of leathery, bright green leaves: on a short (about 1 cm) stem it has one large, 5—6 cm long rich azure blue flower. It is an early spring mountain plant, flowering from April to the summer depending on the conditions and altitude of its habitat. It is usually found at an altitude of about 600—2,000 m above sea level, exceptionally at lower altitudes. This precious plant is protected by law in most European states where it is native.

A very similar species growing in non-calcareous ground is the **Stemless Gentian** (*Gentiana acaulis* L.), which is also protected. It was once also found in lower-lying meadows in the White Carpathians in south-eastern Moravia (today it is extinct there).

An Arctic-Alpine species is the short, slender, annual herb the **Snow Gentian** (*Gentiana nivalis* L.). Branched or unbranched, erect stems bear throughout June-August solitary, intense blue flowers with a narrow tube and spreading pointed lobes, 6—8 mm in size. In Britain this is a very rare protected species included in the British Red Data Book. About eight colonies have been recorded on rock ledges on mountains in Perthshire and Angus, three of which are protected in National Nature Reserves. Botanists believe that this species has greatly declined because of collecting and heavy grazing. It is now one of the rarest British mountain plants, still heavily threatened by collectors.

Of the taller gentians growing in European mountain ranges, a well-known species is the **Spotted Gentian** (*Gentiana punctata* L.). It is a herb with a thick, multi-headed underground rhizome from which thick, slightly angular and hollow unbranched stems 0.25—0.5 m in height grow pale green ovate leaves with distinct parallel veins; the leaves are opposite, the upper half-clasping the stem. Pale yellow and dark violet spotted (hence the name) cylindrical to campanulate flowers, with a 2—4 cm long corolla bloom throughout the summer — from July to September — in clusters at the base of the upper leaves and at the tops of the stems.

The Spotted Gentian is an Alpine species. In central and western Europe it is found in the Alps and

◁ The Pannonian Gentian (*Gentiana pannonica*), with brownish red to violet flowers is also characterised by corollas which are spotted on the outside and by its 5 to 8 recurved calyx lobes.

The Arnica (*Arnica montana*) grows, when in flower, ▷ 20 to 60 cm high; it is found — more and more rarely — in certain types of meadows from lowlands to mountains.

The Scherfel Pasque Flower (*Pulsatilla scherfeli*) has ▷ ▷ fully developed leaves when in flower, basal leaves and three leaves higher up on the stem; all are divided into narrow pointed divisions.

Carpathians and as a rarity also in some mid-altitude mountains. It is a characteristic species of poorer mountain meadows with the communities of the orders of the Mat-grass (*Nardus stricta* L.) and of the Curved Sedge (*Carex curvula* All.). It grows in deep, clay, non-calcareous acid, slightly damp soils. Usually it is found at altitudes of about 1,500 m to almost 2,500 m above sea level.

The Spotted Gentian became almost extinct in several regions where it was picked for its roots. It was used as a medicinal plant and particularly for the production of bitter liqueurs. It is protected in all European countries where it is native.

However, the most important medicinal plant and also a significant resource for the production of stomach liqueurs is the **Great Yellow Gentian** (*Gentiana lutea* L.), which is also protected in those countries where it grows and slightly resembles the previous species. Of all the European Gentians it is the most robust perennial, up to 1.5 m high. Its flowers have a golden yellow rotate corolla. It is a pre-Alpine to Alpine species of mountain meadows and pastures (where it grows at an altitude of up to about 2,000 m above sea level) and also in mountain woods and foothill grassland hillsides and glades in the Alps. Its eastern Carpathian range (in the Poloninski Carpathians in the Ukraine; on the red list there) does not penetrate central Europe. Its occurrence in Thuringia, eastern Germany, or a recently recorded one in the Czech Giant Mountains is evidently of naturalized origin, as in the lower sites of Germany (particularly in the Hessen highland). The Great Yellow Gentian is used as a medicinal herb. The rhizome contains substances which stimulate digestion and the formation of red and white blood cells. It was also often cultivated as an aromatic herb.

Two of the taller European mountain Gentians have dark purple flowers. These are hairless perennials of over 0.5 m in height with simple, thick, erect and hollow stems and with more or less sessile opposite leaves and flowers of 3 to 5 cm in length, blooming in clusters at the base of the upper leaves in July and August. Both species grow on mountain meadows and pastures on non-calcareous, clay or loam, slightly damp soils.

The **Pannonian Gentian** (*Gentiana pannonica* Scop.) has flowers of a dirty brownish red-violet colour with more or less evident spots and 5—8 calyx splits. In spite of its name, the Pannonian Gentian does not grow in Hungary. It is an eastern Alpine species with an islet range in the Bavarian Forest and the adjacent Bohemian Forest. It grows at 1,200 to 2,000 m above sea level. After the Second World War it also appeared in the Bohemian Giant Mountains, but was planted there in the same way as the Great Yellow Gentian. The Pannonian Gentian is also an important medicinal and aromatic plant. It is protected by law in Switzerland, Germany, the Czech Republic and Austria.

Even more restricted in range is the similar **Purple Gentian** (*Gentiana purpurea* L.) with calyxes split down one side and flowers that are reddish on the outside and yellowish on the inside. It is a western-Alpine species growing at somewhat higher altitudes (1,500—2,500 m above sea level). It greatly resembles the Spotted Gentian (except for the colour of the flowers) and the Pannonian Gentian. It is only found in the Alps, is protected by law in France and in Switzerland and in Germany where it grows in the Allgau Alps (but not further eastwards).

The very decorative **Arnica** (*Arnica montana* L.) of the Daisy family (*Compositae*) also has its place next to gentians in the herbal and spice apothecary. It resembles the Leopard's Bane or the yellow Ox-eye Daisy. It is a perennial with a cylindrical rhizome and a ground rosette of ovate, entire, scattered, short-haired leaves. The erect stems with smaller opposite lanceolate leaves are conspicuously glandular, simple or only sparcely branched, growing to a height of about half a metre and ending in large (6—8 cm in diameter) flower heads of dark yellow to

orange coloured flowers. The plant flowers from June to August.

The Arnica is not an exclusively high mountain species, but has the centre of its range in mountainous regions, especially in the Alps (up to over 2,000 m above sea level). Phytogeographers characterize it as a peri-Alpine species (growing on the periphery of high mountains) and also a north-sub-oceanic plant. The core of its range lies in central Europe with extensions running towards the Pyrenees and along the western coast of the Iberian Peninsula. It also penetrates eastern France, is found all over Denmark and in southern Scandinavia. In northern Germany and Poland it also grows in the lowlands, on the Baltic Sea coast and rarely inland. Only a tip of its range enters the central European Carpathians and south-eastern Poland. It occurs also in Belarus, Lithuania and Latvia. The Arnica does not grow in Slovakia and only rarely on the Alpine foothills in western Hungary. It grows on unfertilized poor meadows and pastures as a characteristic species of Mat-grass meadows and on damper boggy meadows, heaths and drier peat-bogs. Also in open woodland, on wood margins and glades. It is more common in damp regions with abundant rainfall.

Formerly Arnica was not that rare an occurrence in Europe. However, people picked it so intensively as a medicinal plant (in the Giant Mountains in particular by the Silesian 'Guild of laboratory Technicians' which we mentioned at the beginning of this chapter) that in many regions entire populations were weakened and even destroyed. In the lowlands and lower mountain areas more intensive farming is having a destructive impact on the plant, particularly fertilization, which the Arnica cannot stand. So it would appear that only high mountains particularly their large-scale protected areas remain as a sanctuary for this very important genetic natural resource. The Arnica is found on most European red lists and is protected by law in all the countries where it grows.

Today the flowers and rhizomes of this strongly aromatic herb are collected and used only in selected regions where the use can be controlled. The herb is also experimentally cultivated. The drug has a sharp, spicy and bitter taste. It is very powerful so it must only be used as prescribed by the doctor. It is a part of many medicaments and in recent years has also been used as an aromatic and tonic ingredient for soaps, bubble baths, shampoos and colognes. The drug contains aromatic oils and bitter essences, tannins and other biochemical and mineral substances. It stimulates the function of the stomach, intestines and kidneys. When it contacts with the body externally it causes hyperaemia (and even blisters with an overdose). It is also used to treat inflammations, as a disinfectant and for the treatment of wounds, in compresses for inflammations and swellings, against rheumatism and arthritis and also against certain heart complaints. Arnica is cultivated in gardens and rockeries because it is a decorative flower.

In the previous chapter we were acquainted with the Pasque Flowers of the Buttercup family (*Ranunculaceae*). Species growing at lower altitudes have blue flowers, those in high mountains are white and sometimes yellow.

The **Alpine Pasque Flower** (*Pulsatilla alpina*(L.) Del.) is a perennial herb which grows at 10 to 30 cm and higher when in fruit. It has long stalked 3-pinnate leaves and one white top flower of 3 to 6 cm in diameter. It is a spring mountain plant, flowering — locally still in large colonies — from May till July.

Today the Alpine Pasque Flower is considered a 'large species' which experts divide into several smaller species. The true Alpine Pasque Flower, a species of meadows (1,500—2,200 m above sea level), is a calciphilous plant. An endemic of central European highlands (the Vosges, the Harz and the Giant Mountains) and higher Carpathian Mountains is a smaller plant with smaller flowers growing on poor, non-calcareous ground among Mat-grass communities called the **Scherfel Pasque Flower** (*Pulsatilla scherfelii*(Ullep.) Skalický). There is also the very decorative **Yellow Alpine Pasque Flower** (*Pulsatilla apiifolia*(Scop.) Schult.). High mountain Pasque Flowers of this group are decorative mountain flowers protected both as species and in protected areas in all the countries where they occur.

The rare **Spring Pasque Flower** (*Pulsatilla vernalis* (L.) Mill.) has hairy 1.5 to 3 m long petal-like segments which are white inside, flashed with violet or pink outside. It is a perennial herb with flowers on short (5—15 cm) stems which are extended when in fruit and with leathery, pinnately lobed leaves with 3—5 oblong leaflets. The period of flowering differs according to the site and altitude of the habitat, from the end of April till July.

The Alpine variety grows in the mountains — the high mountain **Alpine Spring Pasque Flower** (*Pulsatilla vernalis* var. *alpestris* Aichele et Schwegler.). It grows rarely in alpine to nival belts of the Alps (up to 3,500 m above sea level), and also in other mountains of central and north-western Europe. An even

more rare species, very sensitive to the pollution of its environment by agricultural chemicals, is the upland variety — The **Early Spring Pasque Flower** (*Pulsatilla vernalis* var. *vernalis*). In eastern Germany the Spring Pasque Flower is considered a missing species, only some sites in Bavaria and Upper Austria survive; it is rapidly on the decrease in Poland. Of almost a hundred previously known stations in northern, western and particularly southern Bohemia, only three or four remain, with critically weak populations. At the present time nature conservationists are struggling for the preservation of the decorative species, in both its varieties by careful management of protected areas and special cultivation to restore the declining wild native populations. These efforts are made all the more difficult in view of the species, considerable sensitivity to even an insignificant amount of calcium (it is basically a calcifuge species) and (when cultivated in botanical gardens) its tendency to hybridize with nearby other cultivated species, thereby losing its genetic identity.

Of the Anemones (*Anemone* genus), close relatives of the Pasque Flowers, there is the remarkable **Narcissus-flowered Anemone** (*Anemone narcissiflora* L.) found in European mountains. The conspicuous feature of this species (today also classified as a separate *Anemonastrum* genus) is an umbel of 4 to 8 white flowers on 3—4 cm long thin stalks. The flowers grow at the base of sub-floral whorls of toothed bracts on the top of the up to 0.5 m high stems and bloom from the end of spring to the beginning of summer — from May till July.

Narcissus-flowered Anemone is an Alpine-Altai species. It is found in all European high mountains, in the Alps and Carpathians. It grows on mountain meadows in damp habitats on both calcareous and acid ground, in stony and clay-loam soils. It never

◁ ◁ The Spring Pasque Flower (*Pulsatilla vernalis*) is a perennial covered by dense hairs, with large flowers which are pinkish to violet in colour on the outside; the leathery ground leaves develop fully only after flowering, but hibernate the following winter.

◁ The Narcissus-flowered Anemone (*Anemone narcissiflora*) has a conspicuous umbel of 4 to 8 white flowers growing from the base of a whorl of toothed leaves; a typical species of high mountain meadows, it also grows in central European mountains, often in large colonies.

The False Musk Orchid (*Chamorchis alpina*), a small ▽ orchid with its inconspicucous greenish flowers, grows in the north of Europe and in the Alps and Carpathians above the upper tree-limit.

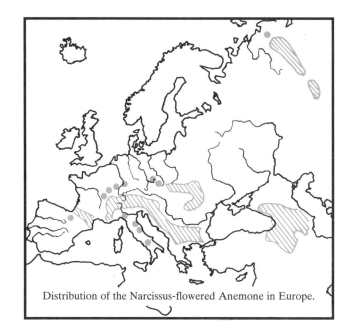

Distribution of the Narcissus-flowered Anemone in Europe.

grows in great abundance, although it does occur in large colonies locally. In the Alps it grows at altitudes up to 2,500 m above sea level. Its lower occurrence line is about 600 m above sea level because the species also grows in central European highlands — the Vosges, the Jura, the Giant Mountains and Jeseníky Mountains. In Switzerland and the German Jura there are also rare relict stations in rather dry grassland with the Upright Brome. These sites, which deserve care and conservation, are mostly under special territorial protection. The Narcissus-flowered Anemone is protected by law in all central European countries where it grows. The herb is poisonous containing protoanemonine in all its parts. The cultivation of this decorative plant in gardens and rockeries is difficult, nevertheless it is sometimes cultivated in gardens in Britain. When cultivated at

lower altitudes the Narcissus-flowered Anemone loses its characteristic appearance and flowers badly.

Not even high mountain are without the presence of terrestrial orchids (*Orchidaceae*). A typical mountain species in central and north-western Europe is the **False Musk Orchid** (*Chamaeorchis alpina* (L.) L.C. Rich.). It is one of the smaller orchids of European flora, only 5—10 cm, rarely up to 15 cm high. This perennial herb has underground, orbicular, undivided tubers and narrowly linear, grass-like leaves, often exceeding the lax in length and a short (up to 3 cm) floral spike composed of 6—14 tiny yellowish green flowers. It blooms in July and August, but it is a highly inconspicuous plant, so it often escapes attention.

The False Musk Orchid is an Alpine-Arctic species with a certain sub-oceanic tendency in its geographical distribution. It grows in the Alps and in only one central European Carpathian mountain range — the Belianske Tatras of the Slovak Tatra National Park. Apart from central Europe, it is also found in the Romanian Carpathians at altitudes of 1,500 m above sea level, exclusively on limestone ground, in stony habitats among Hard-Sedge (*Carex firma* Host), or the Mountain Avens (*Dryas octopetala* L.). It is a plant which is highly tolerant to low temperatures. It is also found in Scandinavia and in isolated stations in the northern European part of Russia. In Germany and on the territory of the Tatra National Park in Slovakia it is protected by law. Of course territorial protection in national parks and reserves is an effective way of its preservation.

A species growing more often, sometimes in large colonies in European mountains, is the vanilla-scented **Black Vanilla Orchid** (*Nigritella nigra* (L.) L.C. Rich.). It is also a relatively short (up to 20 cm high) perennial herb with grasslike leaves which in

157

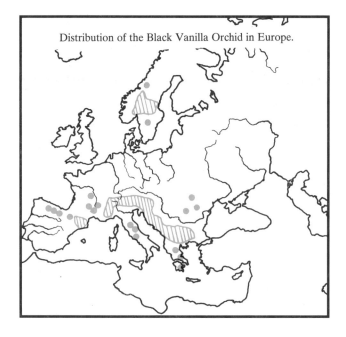

Distribution of the Black Vanilla Orchid in Europe.

length do not exceed the dense orbicular to short cylindrical inflorescence composed of tiny dark violet-purple to blackish crimson flowers. It blooms from July till August.

The Black Vanilla Orchid is an Alpine-Arctic plant. It grows in meadows and pastures at an altitude of 1,000 to 2,800 m above sea level on fresh, often calcareous and clay soils which are rich in nutrients. Its range extends from Greece to the Pyrenees right up to Scandinavia where it descends to lower altitudes. The Black Vanilla Orchid is also quite abundant in the Alps and the Jura. Only temporary occurrences are reported from the Alpine foothills (Alpenvorland) and the Black Forest.

A rarer species is the red-flowering **Red Vanilla Orchid** (*Nigritella miniata* (Crantz) Janchen). It flowers earlier and occurs only in the central and eastern Alps and in the Romanian Carpathians.

Both species of the Vanilla Orchid are protected by law in Switzerland, Germany and Austria.

The delicate **Alpine Cortusa** (*Cortusa matthioli* L.) is a member of the Primrose family (*Primulaceae*). It has pinkish-violet nodding campanulate flowers in a 5—12-flowered umbel at the top of a 10 to 40 cm high scape. It is a perennial covered with soft hairs, glandular, with a rosette of large ground long-stalked leaves with kidney-shaped round blades with toothed margins. It flowers, depending on the location of its habitat, from May till August.

The Alpine Cortusa is a European species found in larger European mountain ranges around springs, in tall damp meadows, in wood and scrub of Green Alder (*Alnus viridis* (Chaix) DC.). It always requires sufficient damp, semi-shaded to shaded habitats. That is why it grows very well in deep rock gorges along which it descends in the Carpathians deep down into lower areas. In the Carpathians it is evi-

dently a distinctly calcicole species. Apart from the Carpathians, it grows in central Europe in the Alps up to about 2,000 m above sea level. It is protected by law in Germany, Austria and the Czech and Slovak Republics. What is highly remarkable is the sole relict occurrence in the Czech Republic of the species at the bottom of the famous karstic Macocha Abyss in the Protected Landscape Area of Moravian karst where it grows at an unusually low altitude of just over 350 metres. The local plants were described as a special subspecies of the Moravian Cortusa

◁ The Alpine Cortusa (*Cortusa matthioli*), an attractive mountain plant of the Primrose family, actually does resemble the primrose; it is a hairy perennial with conspicuously large, long-stalked basal rounded leaves with lobed margins.

◁ The Red Vanilla Orchid (*Nigritella miniata*) is an orchid
▽ of mountain meadows with grassy leaves and a short cylindrical dense inflorescence of numerous small, pinkish red flowers. The more abundant Black Vanilla Orchid differs in the colour of its very dark crimson black flowers and shorter more globose inflorescence.

The Alpine Aster (*Aster alpinus*) belongs to the most ▷ decorative of Alpine plants; the large solitary bluish violet flower heads with yellow discs bloom at the top of short, erect stems.

(*Cortusa matthioli* L. subsp. *moravica* (Podpěra) Soják).

There is an ornamental rockery plant which resembles a violet-blue ox-eye daisy with a golden-yellow disk. This is the **Alpine Aster** (*Aster alpinus* L.) of the Daisy family (*Compositae*). It is a short, hairy perennial only 5−20 cm high, with erect or ascendant usually unbranched stems ending with solitary flower head of 3 to 5 cm in diameter. The marginal rays of the flower head are usually violet-blue, more rarely pink or pure white. The plant flowers from May till August, according to the habitat location, particularly the altitude.

The Alpine Aster is widespread in Eurasia and the western part of North America. The centre of its range was formerly considered to be central Asia. However, new research shows that the species is actually a group of 'small' species. For in central Europe various differences appear between the Alpine, Carpathian and highland populations. In the Alps, Jura and Carpathians the Alpine Aster is clearly a calcicole plant. It usually grows in rocky, sunny habitats from 1,000 to 3,000 m above sea level. Locally it descends through gorges to lower altitudes, in Austria growing at 200 m above sea level. It is protected by law in Switzerland, Austria, the Czech Republic, the Slovak Republic and Poland. In the Czech Republic scattered occurrences of the Alpine Aster on the rocky igneous summits of the České středohoří lie between 400 and 800 m above sea level, all being preserved in protected areas. As a glacial relict, the Alpine Aster is also found in similar rocky sites in the Thuringian Upland. In eastern Germany it is on the red list as a potentially threatened species, the famous Thuringian locality of Bohlen (340 m above sea level) in the Gera district is a nature reserve. What was remarkable (but obviously not newly confirmed) was the isolated occurrence of the plant in the Velká kotlina (Large Kettle) Reserve at Hrubý Jeseník. There were once reports of the Alpine Aster in the Sudeten Mountains, and also on the Polish side of the Giant Mountains. While the Alpine Aster has a chance of survival in high mountains, particularly in national parks and reserves, relict occurrence of the species in European highlands and uplands require special attention and protection.

However, let us return to the Primrose family, this time to its nominal genus, *Primula*. We have already been acquainted with some of the representatives of the genus in previous chapters. But Primroses also have a significant presence in the high mountains.

The **Smallest Primrose** (*Primula minima* L.) is really a small, short (1 to 5 cm) perennial herb, growing in tufted cushions. The leathery obovate leaves are composed in ground rosettes from which thin stalks emerge bearing bright red, more rarely pinkish or completely white flowers with a long corolla tube and flat bifid lobes. The flowers open up in the summer months of July and August.

It is a species of the eastern Alps, also growing in the Czech-Polish Giant Mountains and in the mountains of the Balkan Peninsula. It grows on non-calcareous Alpine meadows and in rock and scree habitats. It is a plant which is highly tolerant of the harsh mountain climate and of rather exposed habitats, but demands a certain degree of moisture particularly in the soil. It grows from 800 to 3,000 m above sea level. In the Carpathians it is one of the vascular plants growing on the highest peaks. The Smallest Primrose is protected in Germany, Austria, the Czech Republic and Poland.

In Switzerland all red-flowering mountain species of Primroses, which look very much like the Smallest Primrose, are protected. Today, of the central and western European mountain ranges, several species of Primroses occur only in the Alps and most of them are also protected in Germany and Austria. A rock plant of the nival belt is the highly decorative, up to 7 cm high **Hairy Primrose** (*Primula hirsuta* All.), which is usually found growing in rows in rocky cre-

vices. The pink **Clusian Primrose** (*Primula clusiana* Tausch) grows on rock walls, scree and meadows. Some Italian and Balkan endemic mountain primroses are included in the European botanical red list.

In Scandinavia, an attractive plant of calcareous mountain rocks is the red **Scandinavian Primrose** (*Primula scandinavica* Brunn), similar to the Scottish Primrose, but taller.

A highly decorative plant of mountain rocks, when in flower (from April till June), is the shiny yellow **Auricula** (*Primula auricula* L.). Even when not in flower, it has an attractive rosette of broad, fleshy, smooth to glossy green, sometimes mealy-white leaves. Another English name of this plant is the Bear's-ear. In gardens this 5—20 cm high perennial is often cultivated for decoration with a wide range of flower colours. It has pleasantly scented flowers.

The centre of range of the Auricula are the Alps where it ascends to over 2,500 m above sea level. It is a pioneer plant of rocky habitats. It roots in crevices of steep, bare, often fully sunlit rocks (the succulent structure of the leaves adapts it to this type of habitat) as well as on shady mossy walls in the thin surface layer of fine soil and humus. At the same time, it is an exclusively calcicole plant. It descends to lower Alpine foothills not only in gorges, but also in swampy meadows. Although sometimes described as an Alpine endemic, the Auricula also occurs in the French and Swiss Jura. It also grows in the Black Forest and in the Italian Apennines. There is an isolated range in the Carpathians. From Slovakia this species penetrates (through the bilateral Biosphere Reserve of Slovak Karst — Aggetelék) into northern Hungary where plants of the Carpathian populations were described as a different subspecies called the Hungarian Auricula (*Primula auricula* L. subsp. *hungarica* (Borb.) Soó). In most central European countries in which the Auricula is native, it is protected by law. Its occurrence in areas at lower altitudes, particularly of a relict type, provided the motivation or at least part of the motivation for the establishment of protected areas.

Only in the alpine or nival belt in the central Alps in central and north-western Europe can one find a species, growing in silicate, non-calcareous rock plant communities, called the **Dwarf Forget-me-not** (*Eritrichium nanum* (L.) Schrad ex Gaud.) of the Borage family (*Boraginaceae*). This delicate Alpine plant really does look like a tiny forget-me-not. It is a cushion-like perennial only 1—5 cm high with leaves and stems covered with soft, silky hairs and bright, forget-me-not blue flowers. In Switzerland it is protected by law.

Nothing so fully and precisely expresses the character of high mountain rock plants as the name of perhaps the most numerous, diverse and loveliest of plant genera, the Saxifrages (*Saxifraga*, which in Latin means the 'rock-breaker'; 'Steinbrech' in German, with equivalents in several other languages). The plants of the Saxifrage family have 5-part flowers which are usually highly decorative in species of the Saxifrage genus. The general impression is also often augmented by the very low and tiny growth of the plants and the large number of flowers. The Saxifrages are popular garden flowers, particularly for rockeries. Numerous cultivars have been produced and special books have been published on them. However, the greatest enjoyment from these mountain gems is coming across them in their natural environment.

The **Purple Saxifrage** (*Saxifraga oppositifolia* L.) is a perennial, sparsely tufted herb with creeping stems and opposite leaves. It usually has small lime-encrusted pores on the tips of the leaves. The solitary

Distribution of the Purple Saxifrage in Europe.

◁ ◁ The Smallest Primrose (*Primula minima*) has bright purplish pink flowers with five two-lobed petals; a rosette of tough toothed leaves forms tufts and even cushions.

◁ The Auricula (*Primula auricula*), a species of mountain rock habitats, has yellow flowers; it is identified by its basal rosette of broad, glabrous and fleshy leaves.

The Purple Saxifrage (*Saxifraga oppositifolia*) has pale ▽ pink to deep purple flowers; the flowers grow individually on short flower-bearing stems, the main stems form carpet-like cushions and are creeping, covered by small greyish green opposite leaves.

flowers on 0.5—5 cm long stems measure 1—1.5 cm in diameter. The petals are pinkish purple with greyish-violet anthers. The plant flowers from April till July.

It is a variable species with a number of subspecies widespread in the circumpolar region of the Old and New World mountains and in the north (Arctic-Alpine distribution). In central and north-western Europe it grows in rock and stony habitats in the Alps in the alpine and nival belt. It is quite often washed down by rivers onto their gravel terraces at lower altitudes. It is found in glacial corries of the Czech and Polish Giant Mountains at an altitude of 1,100—1,350 m above sea level and in the highest Carpathian Mountain ranges. In the Czech Republic and Germany it is protected by law.

The Purple Saxifrage is abundant in the sub-Arctic and Arctic regions. It is still quite common in Scotland, and also found growing sparsely on some of the higher northern English, Welsh (particularly Snowdonia) and Irish mountains. It is widely cultivated in gardens throughout Britain.

The subspecies (*Saxifraga oppositifolia* L. subsp. *amphibia* (Sunderm.) Br.-Bl.) is included in the European red list. It is an endemic growing on the banks of Lake Constance flooded periodically during the summer. However it is one of the plants found in the 'black' section of red lists because it has apparently definitively become extinct.

In Switzerland and Austria all high mountain species of Saxifrage are protected.

Also in Britain several species of mountain Saxifrages are protected and/or included in the British Red Data Book. The **Irish Saxifrage** (*Saxifraga rosacea* Moench.) is an alpine species found rarely on mountains and sea cliffs in southern and western Ireland. Its sole site in the UK was first discovered in Gwynedd in 1870, but became extinct around 1960. Similar to it is the low, loose, cushion-forming **Tufted Saxifrage** (*Saxifraga caespitosa* L.) with 3-lobed leaves and white or creamish flowers (1—3) on a slightly leafy stem. This plant of mountain rocks, cliffs and moraines, protected in the UK, is known to exist in 14 locations in North Wales and Scotland. The Welsh population was almost destroyed by the summer drought of 1976, whereas Scottish sites have been badly damaged by collectors. The Tufted Saxifrage, popular in gardens, is probably the rarest and most endangered of all British mountain saxifrages. Although protected in two National Nature Reserves and three Sites of Special Scientific Interest, it is believed to be safe only in inaccessible places. It flowers from May to July.

Another British protected species (also in 1 NNR and 4 SSSI) is the **Drooping Saxifrage** (*Saxifraga cernua* L.). This is a low, thin-stemmed perennial with kidney-shaped, 5—7 lobed, long-stalked basal leaves and white, often solitary flowers. This Arctic-Alpine species occurs in corries and crevices in basic

rock in weak populations, all of them confined to the central Scottish Highlands. In spite of all protection, the colonies are continuously being uprooted by alpine gardeners and also botanists. The fourth of the British 'red' mountain Saxifrages is the **Highland Saxifrage** (*Saxifraga rivularis* L.), a hairless, low, tufted perennial with white flowers, an Arctic-Alpine species of wet, rocky mountain habitats, flowering in July and August. It is known to exist in 21 localities in the Highlands of Scotland. Seven of them are protected by established NNR and SSSI, but again it seems their best protection is the inaccessibility of most of them except to skilled mountaineers.

A high mountain species which grows in central Europe also on relict habitats in lower altitudes (a de-Alpine element) is the **Live-long Saxifrage** (*Saxifraga paniculata* Mill.). This perennial is highly decorative with its rosettes of fleshy, greyish green leaves dotted on their margins with white lime-pores. The plants form large tufts and often, particularly in locations at lower altitudes that are frequented by tourists, they form a temptation for being transplanted to rockeries. (It is a truly beautiful rock plant, but this species and various cultivated varieties can normally be purchased in flower and garden centres.) Blooming from May till June, the racemose inflorescence at the top of branched, 10—30 cm high stems, is composed of white, sometimes red spotted flowers measuring about 1 cm in diameter.

This Arctic-Alpine species, widespread in Europe and the eastern part of North America, is variable. It is exclusively a rock plant. It grows in the crevices of sunny rocks as well as in shady mossy rock walls. It is a calcicole species, but grows on different ground, particularly in alkaline, nutrient rich soils, e.g. on basalt. It grows abundantly in the foothills of the Alps and Carpathians through which it penetrates in the

south from Slovakia to northern Hungary and in the north into Poland. It grows at up to 2,500—3,000 m above sea level and descends to 300 m above sea level. It grows in the Vosges and the French mountains southwards, the Black Forest, in several locations in the south-western part of eastern Germany, on the rocks in the valleys of Czech and Moravian rivers in regions of xerotherm vegetation and in the Moravian karst. Visitors to the peak rocks of the Hrubý Jeseník have virtually destroyed all its former sites. It occurs locally in southern Norway. It is protected in most of the countries within its European range.

A highly remarkable species is the **Arctic Saxifrage** (*Saxifraga nivalis* L.), one of the most significant Arctic relicts in central Europe. This low, hairy perennial with a crowded head of white or pink flowers, is rare and local in the Lake District, North

◁ ◁ The Live-long Saxifrage (*Saxifraga paniculata*) has white flowers in rich racemose inflorescence on the end of the stems which grow from decorative basal rosettes of greyish green fleshy leaves. It is a characteristic species of limestone rock habitats.

◁ The Mossy Saxifrage (*Saxifrage bryoides*) corresponds in its appearance to its species name; its small leafy rosettes are grouped into tufts resembling a moss with greenish white flowers. It is a pioneer species of high mountain rock and scree habitats.

◁ The Low Rock-jasmine (*Androsace chamaejasme*) is a
▽ member of the Primrose family: from a basal rosette of narrow lanceolate leaves grows a short, hairy scape bearing a lax umbel with pure white flowers which have a distinct yellow eye.

The Petrocallis (*Petrocallis pyrenaica*), belongs to the ▽ Cress family; four-part pinkish violet flowers densely cover the cushion-like tufts of this pioneer plant of high mountain rock and scree habitats.

The Baldo Sedge (*Carex baldensis*) is a decorative and ▷ conspicuous high mountain species from a less attractive ▽ family: its orbicular white inflorescences are conspicuous. This perennial grows only in the Alps.

Distribution of the Petrocallis in Europe.

Wales, Scottish Highlands and Co. Sligo in Ireland.

The **Low Rock-jasmine** (*Androsace chamaejasme* Wolf.) of the Primrose family (*Primulaceae*) differs from the saxifrages in its white to pinkish tubular corollas with a distinct yellowish orange stain in the mouth. The tiny, deep green basal rosettes of this perennial have leaves with hairy margins. Erect scapes of up to 10 cm in length grow from these rosettes. The scapes bear a dense umbel of flowers measuring about 1 cm in diameter. The flowers bloom from June to July.

The Low Rock-jasmine is an Alpine-Altai circumpolar plant. In central Europe it is found in the Alps and Carpathians in the alpine or nival belt. It grows in open grassland communities in shallow, mainly calcareous soils on rock and scree. All species of the Rock-jasmines (*Androsace*) are protected in

Switzerland and Austria. In the Swiss and Austrian Alps grow the dense cushion-like species with large flowers: the **Swiss Rock-jasmine** (*Androsace helvetica* (L.) All), the pink **Alpine Rock-jasmine** (*Androsace alpina* (L.) Lam.) and the deep red **Pink Rock-jasmine** (*Androsace carnea* L.). All these plants are much sought-after by rockery gardeners and therefore are threatened in the wild.

The 4-part flowers typical of the Cress family (*Brassicaceae*) distinguish the **Petrocallis** (*Petrocallis pyrenaica* (L.) R.Br.) from the similar cushion-forming rock-jasmines. It is a tufted and cushion-forming, only 2—8 cm high perennial with tough, 3- to 5-lobed leaves in basal rosettes. Scapes grow from the centre of the rosettes bearing several lilac pinkish-violet flowers measuring 1—2 cm in diameter. They bloom in June and July.

163

◁ The Roseroot (*Rhodiola rosea*) resembles the Stone-crops (*Sedum*) to which it is closely related; it is a fleshy leaved plant with yellow to yellowish orange flowers.

The Glacier Crowfoot (*Ranunculus glacialis*) bears ▽ large, white and pink tinted flowers in rock crevices high above the upper tree-line; it holds the record for being the highest-altitude flowering plant growing at 4,275 m above sea level.

The Alpine Willow (*Salix alpina*) is one of several low ▷ creeping high mountain willows, all of which need protection; the entire leaves with hairy margins develop at the same time as the brownish violet catkins.

Distribution of the Roseroot in Europe.

The Petrocallis is an Alpine, strictly calcicole species growing in the Pyrenees, the Alps and the Carpathians. It grows in rock crevices, on scree and grit. It is protected by law in Switzerland.

The succulent **Roseroot** (*Rhodiola rosea* L.) of the Stonecrop family (*Crassulaceae*) also belongs to the relatives of succulent Stonecrops (*Sedum*). It is a perennial, 10 to 40 cm high herb which, from a branched fleshy rhizome (when broken gives off a rose-like fragrance, from which the English name derives), grows a tuft of erect unbranched succulent stems with thick alternate fleshy leaves. The tiny 4-part flowers with yellowish to reddish corollas are composed in dense top clusters. It flowers from June to July.

The Roseroot is an Arctic-Alpine circumpolar species. In central and north-western Europe it is found in the Alps, the Carpathians and in some lower mountain ranges (the Vosges, the Black Forest, the Sudetens) on damp, somewhat shaded rocky and scree habitats. In Scandinavia, the Roseroot, growing in Europe up to 3,000 m altitute, occurs at the northern border of its rangeas as low

as sea level. In Britain the species is still quite abundant in the Highlands of Scotland, where it descends also to the maritime cliffs of western Scotland. Scattered sites are found in the mountains of nothern England, northern Wales and western Ireland. It is rare in and is disappearing from the lower mountains in central Europe. It is considered an important medicinal plant. It contains similar substances to the stonecrops and these are used mainly in folk medicine against the widest variety of diseases including cancer, so this led to a strong depletion in its populations in certain regions.

The Buttercups and Crowfoots (*Ranunculus*) — the nominal genus of the Buttercup family (*Ranunculaceae*) — also include several typical high mountain species. The prettiest of these is the **Glacier Crowfoot** (*Ranunculus glacialis* L.). As the

165

Distribution of the Baldo Sedge in Europe.

The Baldo Sedge is an endemic of the Alps. It not
only occurs in limestone and dolomitic soils in the
open grassland communities of the Sesleria and
Evergreen Sedge (*Carex sempervirens*) on rock and
stony ground, in the sub-Alpine belt (800—1,500 m
above sea level), but also in heather pine woods (the
Erico-Pinion order). In some places in the Alpine
foothills of Bavaria and Austria it is washed down to
the gravel banks of Alpine rivers. It is more abundant
in the south-eastern Alps. In Switzerland, where
there is one solitary site at Ofenpass, it is protected
by law.

Three mountain sedges occurring in the Highlands of Scotland are included in the British Red
Data Book. Probably the most rare among them is
the **Close-headed Alpine-sedge** (*Carex norvegica*
Retz.). This slender tufted perennial with short
leaves and 3 ovoid dark brown or black spikelets
grows in small quantities on wet ledges and on rocky
slopes in the higher mountains of Perthshire, Angus
and Aberdeenshire. It was heavily over-collected in
the past, and is now protected in one National Nature Reserve and four Sites of Special Scientific
Interest. The **Bristle Sedge** (*Carex microglochin*
Wahlenberg), a small stiff slender species with a solitary, terminal, bright brown spikelet, is a circumpolar Artic-Alpine species, flowering in summer. It
grows at over 800 m above sea level in stony mica-
ceous flushes in the mountains of Perthshire. The
Hare's-foot Sedge (*Carex lachenalii* Schkuhr.) is
a creeping perennial of rocky ledges and high-level

name indicates, it is one of the high mountain species
of vascular plants growing at the highest levels in
close proximity to glaciers and eternal snow fields.
Sometimes during the night frosts, its flowers freeze
so that in the morning the white to pinkish petals are
brittle as though made of glass. It is a perennial which
is only 10 to 15 cm high with deeply 3-lobed thick
basal leaves and an erect, one to three flowered stem.
The large flowers, measuring up to 3 cm in diameter,
bloom in July and August.

This Arctic-Alpine species of silicate rock crevices and scree, growing at the highest levels of the
Alps and Carpathians, holds the record among European high mountain plants, by growing at the
highest altitudes. In the Bernese Alps in Switzerland
it was recorded at 4,274 m above sea level (on the
Finsteraarhorn). It is also one of several flowering
plant species growing on the highest Tatra peak
— Mount Gerlach (2,655 m above sea level). So in
the Alps it occurs at 500—1,000 m above the average
eternal snow-line. In Scandinavia it can be found at
much lower altitudes. It does not occur, however, in
the Faeroes or Iceland. It is clear that this remarkably
vital plant deserves strict protection. It is protected
by legal regulations in Austria and in the territory of
the Tatra National Park in Slovakia.

In the central European high mountains **Baldo
Sedge** (*Carex baldensis* L.) of the Sedge family
(*Cyperaceae*) belongs to those protected plants
which, owing to their grass-like appearance, usually
escape attention. But at a closer glance it is in fact
a rather decorative plant and is sometimes cultivated
in Alpine gardens (thereby obviously an endangered
species in the wild). It is a 10 to 30 cm high perennial
with orbicular inflorescence of white spikelets from
which range three pale yellow stigmas. It flowers in
July.

Distribution of the Parsley Fern in Europe.

flushes in areas where there are extremely late snow patches. About 10 colonies are known in Angus, Aberdeenshire, Banffshire, Inverness-shire and Argyllshire, six of them covered by protected areas, some however subject to much public pressure. We should probably also mention the fourth 'red' species — the **Mountain Bog-sedge** (*Carex rariflora* (Wahlenb.) Sm.) occurring at about 30 sites on slopes of oligotrophic peat in the Scottish Highlands.

Interesting characteristic plants of the sub-Alpine, Alpine and nival belts of high mountains are tiny creeping herb-like willows. These are the lowest central and northwest European woody plants of Arctic-Alpine or Alpine distribution, and deserve careful protection, because they are substantially declining as a result of the impact of civilization on the mountain habitats.

The **Alpine Willow** (*Salix alpina* Scop.) of the Willow family (*Salicaceae*) is a creeping or low spreading shrub only 10—30 cm high with densely leafed branches. The short-stalked, obovate to lanceolate leaves are about 3 cm wide and 5 cm long. From May to July catkins appear on the bush together with the leaves.

An Alpine species, the Alpine Willow grows in central Europe in the Alps and the Carpathians in the sub-Alpine to Alpine belt on damp meadows and often among dwarf pines. On the German red list it is classified as a potentially endangered species.

Like Alpine Willow, but with toothed leaves is the **Whortle-leaved Willow** (*Salix myrsinites* L.). This Arctic species which occurs in Scandinavia is rare and localised in Scotland from Argyll and Perth to Orkney.

On the territory of the Tatra National Park in the High Tatras, all low mountain species of willows are protected by law. The most remarkable is the low creeping **Net-leaved Willow** (*Salix reticulata* L.), an Arctic-Alpine species with rounded leaves with a distinctly impressed venation, and the Arctic-Alpine shrub with bright, shiny, green, hairless leaves called the **Dwarf Willow** (*Salix herbacea* L.)

Both the above willows are native in the British flora. The Dwarf Willow is locally abundant from Wales and north England northwards and in Ireland. The Net-leaved Willow is only very localised in Scotland: it was considered for inclusion into the British Red Data Book, like the much-branched creeping **Mountain Willow** (*Salix arbuscula* L.), very localised in Scotland. However, the only 'red' British willow is the **Woolly Willow** (*Salix lanata* L.). This is a higher shrub (up to 3 m) with stout branches and large woolly buds. Thick yellow catkins (2.5—4 cm long) appear before the leaves. This Arctic species extending from Iceland east to the Altai mountains is in Britain confined to a few rocky alpine glens in Scotland. The European red list contains the mountain shrub called the **Two-Coloured Willow** (*Salix bicolor* Ehrh.). This bush grows in flushes. It does not grow in the Alps but is found in the central French mountains, in the Black Forest and the Harz (critically endangered in eastern Germany, it is cultivated in a protective culture at the Halle an der Saale Botanical Gardens).

Of the ferns that inhabit the boulder screes in the treeless areas of the mountain and sub-alpine belt of central Europe, we should mention the highly decorative **Parsley Fern** (*Cryptogramma crispa* (L.) R. Br.) of the Parsley Fern family (*Cryptogrammaceae*). This is a perennial plant with non-hibernating, 15 to 30 cm long yellowish green, two to four times pinnate stalked leaves. It is remarkable for its different fruiting fronds with sori.

The Parsley Fern is a typical boreo-alpine species with a certain sub-oceanic tendency of distribution. In the west it extends as far as the British Isles. It is rare in central and western England, in Ireland, more frequent in northern England and Scotland. It is a plant which is intolerant of summer heat and heavy grazing. It grows on non-calcareous ground, in the central Alps up to 3,000 m above sea level, more rarely in the central European mountain ranges of the Vosges, the Black Forest, the Hohe Venn, the Bavarian Forest and the adjacent Bohemian Forest, in the Novohradské and the Giant Mountains. In the Czech Republic it is protected by law and is critically endangered in both the Czech and the Slovak Republics. The only known occurrence in the Carpathians is at Ďumbier in the Low Tatras (today a National Park). It is also protected by law in Germany (on the red list marked as 'potentially endangered').

POSTSCRIPT

Slender Iris (*Iris pumila*) grows on grassy and rocky steppes in central and south-eastern Europe. It has large flowers in a great variety of colour — ranging from white-yellow to dark violet in colour with relatively short, broad leaves.

You have read the book and we do not suppose you read it all at once. It is not a book that should be read like a novel. The reader should reach for it when he returns from a walk through nature or from holiday, so that he can refresh his knowledge, learn more about plants and also become aware of the seriousness of the situation in which nature finds itself today. The contents of the book are not pleasing. We wanted to show, by presenting the facts, that nature is being more and more seriously damaged by human activities. One of the saddest results of human civilisation is the extinction of organisms — plants, fungi and animals. As stressed in the introduction to this book, this is not only a case of aesthetic or cultural losses, but there is also a danger that the entire process of the impoverishment of nature may have serious socio-economic consequences.

After reading the book you must automatically ask yourself this question: What can I — as a citizen and nature lover — do? The answer to this question is usually a pessimistic one. Most people think that nature conservation — and environmental protection as a whole — is the affair of the state authorities and institutions and is beyond the power of the individual. It is indisputable that the process of the constant impoverishment of nature results mostly from the construction of industrial plants, urbanization, open-pit mining, intensive farming and other authority-level activities. Nevertheless each one of us can effectively contribute towards nature conservation by becoming actively and socially involved, and by behaving in such a way as to disturb the countryside and its inhabitants as little as possible.

At the present time there are many organizations in the world engaged in nature conservation or environmental protection which have attained more than one important success. These voluntary organizations associate nature lovers and they are on the increase. The fact that something disturbing is occurring in nature should become the stimulus for everyone to report such cases to the appropriate organization. It should be a lesson to many who perhaps, without being aware, are causing damage to nature, and could instead aid in the preservation of a rare population. It is enough just to see how hikers make shortcuts through the countryside at spots where access is prohibited. The same applies to littering the countryside which, in time, leads to the excessive feeding (eutrophication) of the soil particularly with nitrogen, and this is finally used by ruderal plants. Their expansion, is very strong in some places and they aggressively force out rare or even threatened plants. Many localities formerly blooming with diverse vegetation, for example in recreational areas, have long since been transformed into monotonous stands of plants.

If a person wants to become an active nature conservationist, he or she must possess a certain knowledge of nature. We want to contribute to this with our book and help people to acquire this knowledge. We have tried not only to present information about rare and threatened plant species, but have also attempted to arouse in the reader the desire to deepen his or her learning of the mysterious laws of plant life. We would be pleased if this book were to prompt some readers to learn more about nature and its conservation.

Věroslav Samek

Further Reading

Blamey M., Grey-Wilson C.: *The Illustrated Flora of Britain and Northern Europe.* Hodder and Stoughton, London 1989.

Fitter A.: *An Atlas of the Wild Flowers of Britain and Northern Europe.* Collins, London 1978.

Gibbons B., Brough P.: *The Hamlyn Photographic Guide to the Wild Flowers of Britain and Northern Europe.* Hamlyn, London 1992.

Milne-Redhead E. (Edit.): *The Conservation of the British Flora.* The Botanical Society of the British Isles, London 1963.

Perring F. (Edit.): *The Flora of a Changing Britain.* The Botanical Society of the British Isles, London 1970.

Perring F., Farrel L.: *British Red Data Books.* 1. *Vascular Plants* (2nd edition). The Royal Society for Nature Conservation, Lincoln 1983.

Perring F., Walters S.M. (Edits.): *Atlas of the British Flora* (3rd edition). EP Publishing Company and The Botanical Society of the British Isles, Wakefield 1983.

Sinker C.A., Packham J.R., Trueman I.C., Oswald P.H., Perring F.H., Prestwood W.V.: *Ecological Flora of the Shropshire Region.* Shropshire Trust for Nature Conservation, Shropshire 1985 (2nd corrected edition 1991).

Tutin T.G., Heywood V.H., Burges N.A., Moore D.M., Valentine D.H., Walters S.M., Webb D.A. (Edits.): *Flora Europaea,* Vols. I—V, consolidated index. Cambridge University Press 1964—1983.

Williams J.G., Williams A.E., Arlott N.: *Orchids of Britain and Europe.* Collins, London 1978.

For more information about and participation in saving wild plants in Britain please contact PLANTLIFE, The Natural History Museum, Cromwell Road, London SW7 5BD, tel. 0171—938 9111.

Index of Common Names

(Page numbers in *italics* refer to captions to illustrations, page numbers in **bold** to main entries.)

172

173

Index of Botanical Names

(Page numbers in *italics* refer to captions to illustrations, page numbers in **bold** to main entries.)

174